CRYPTIC CROSSWORDS
and How to Solve Them

Michael Kindred & Derrick Knight

Chamb

CHAMBERS
An imprint of Chambers Harrap Publishers Ltd
7 Hopetoun Crescent
Edinburgh EH7 4AY

This paperback edition first published by Chambers 1995
Earlier hardback edition published by W & R Chambers Ltd 1993
Reprinted 1993 (twice), 1995, 1996, 1997, 1998 (three times)

A CIP catalogue record for this book
is available from the British Library

ISBN 0-550-19047-3

Editor: David Skinner

Typeset by Roger King Graphic Studios, Poole, Dorset
Printed in England by Clays Ltd, St Ives plc

Preface

This book, which is the result of a long collaboration between Michael and myself, had its origin in the discovery one Sunday morning that we both enjoyed the intriguing world of cryptic crosswords.

During the week which followed, I set a puzzle for Michael; he soon solved it and retaliated. This led to our setting puzzles for each other and offering constructive criticism on how they may be improved. The setting of mine was a pleasant means of whiling away my daily train journey to London. I was interrupted quite often by fellow-commuters who wanted me to explain various clues in most of the daily newspapers. Thus the idea for this book emerged. The gestation period saw many changes from the original concept to what was sent to the publisher, together with many changes from that manuscript to its present form.

David Skinner, who is acknowledged below, is responsible for many helpful suggestions and improvements.

I am indebted to my uncle, the late Bill Burdett, for my two lifelong passions of cricket and crosswords. Michael's first mentor was his grandmother, the late Eneata Holman, on whose knee he sat many a time, generally hindering progress towards completion of the puzzles.

We are also indebted to David Skinner for his knowledgeable, skilful and thorough editing, without which this book would be the poorer. Finally, both Michael and I would like to express our gratitude to the many people who solved the puzzles and monitored them for degree of difficulty – in particular Bill Skinner and Roger and Marcelle King whose assistance has proved invaluable.

Derrick Knight

Contents

Introduction

Cryptic Crosswords and How to Solve Them is designed to teach all the cryptic tricks of the trade through a series of graded puzzles with clues to the clues. We have deliberately kept formal instruction to a minimum since one of the ideas behind the book is the belief that people enjoy actually doing crosswords rather than reading about how to do them. It is also true to say that most people probably learn how to do cryptic crosswords in exactly the sort of way that we have set out to demonstrate here: by studying the solutions and working back through the clues.

This process of induction usually happens in two ways. The dedicated and self-reliant learner will often build up familiarity with clue types by the simple expedient of solving what he or she can, and then trying to work out the structure of the remaining clues by reference to the solution grid when it appears. More commonly, a friend, relative or colleague will introduce a beginner to the joys of solving by providing background information to the various clue types. Practice and enthusiasm gradually produce increased speed and efficiency, and enable the novice to progress to more complicated puzzles. Most people begin solving crosswords through a combination of the two routes described above.

What we have sought to do in this book is to provide a more formal model of this kind of informal familiarization and training process – laid out in a way that provides solvers not only with a programmed learning approach, but with a convenient source of reference to clue types, abbreviations and many of the arcane instruments of the crossword setter's art. (No wonder the two most famous setters' pseudonyms – Ximenes and Torquemada – have their origins in the tortured history of the Inquisition!)

The material is laid out in what we hope is a reasonably logical manner. First of all, we have provided a simple summary of **Cryptic Clue Types and Devices** designed to introduce the solver to all the most commonly encountered clue structures. The listing in this section is comprehensive and practical; it cannot hope to be exhaustive because crossword compilers are a devious bunch and are always trying to come up with some novel device to torment the solver. Nonetheless, our summary is more than adequate as a key to the kind of clues you will encounter in crosswords appearing in the national dailies and, needless to say, it covers all the clues featured in our own puzzles. A summary of the clue types is also printed on a bookmark that accompanies the book: this is intended as a handy reference for the graded puzzles that follow, some of which contain a shorthand indication of clue type as an aid to solving.

The next section gives **Some Practical Advice on Solving**: it tackles some of the methodological and psychological aspects of solving (such as what to do when you get stuck!) as well as providing a necessarily subjective guide to the relative difficulty of a cross-section of crosswords that appear in various daily newspapers.

Now we come to the core of the book: the **Graded Puzzles**. These have been divided into three sections, each of which presents ten puzzles. The first section contains the 'initiation' puzzles – those in which the beginner is offered most help. The initiation puzzles feature: partially completed grids, highlighted indications of definitional elements in the clues, shorthand keys to clue types and, as far as possible, relatively simple clues and solutions.

Crosswords 11 - 20 still retain the bracketed indications of clue types but dispense with the definitional highlighting and 'on-grid' solutions, while the final ten puzzles contain no guidance other than the comprehensive explanations which appear in the **Help** section immediately preceding the **Solutions**. Some of the clues and solutions in these final puzzles are quite tough – so be warned.

In compiling the puzzles we have taken the view that most of the people who will use this book will be wanting to learn or improve their technique for solving crosswords in the 'big' dailies. Therefore, we have tried to set clues that are reasonably representative of the clue types and level of difficulty that solvers will encounter when tackling such puzzles. Since this is the case we recommend that you have available a good English dictionary. The latest edition of *Chambers Dictionary* is comprehensive (including a lot of useful dialect words and usages) and offers good value for money. *Chambers Encyclopedic English Dictionary* has the benefit of encyclopedic entries.

The beginner who works through all thirty puzzles should be equipped to tackle successfully (even if slowly at first) the cryptic puzzles that appear in papers such as the *Daily Telegraph*, *The Guardian*, *Independent* or *Times* – the latter of which is generally acknowledged to be the most consistently challenging.

As additional assistance, the book includes a **Two-way Crossword Glossary**. This is intended as no more than a summary of the most common cryptic indications – but it will certainly prove a useful reference source for the beginner. Those who wish to obtain more comprehensive reference works may go to the **Further Reading and Contacts** section which completes the book. There are various excellent titles recommended here for those who feel themselves destined to become fanatics.

Cryptic Clue Types and Devices

The word 'cryptic' means 'mysteriously obscure, secret, hidden', and the art of setting cryptic crosswords always involves an attempt to mislead the solver in some way. In fact, the best cryptic clues are invariably those that read as apparently normal English sentences or phrases, but which actually indicate a solution that has nothing whatever to do with the obvious literal sense of the clue.

Solvers of ordinary definitional crosswords may well throw up their hands in horror at this deliberate double-speak. To the cryptic fan, however, such dissimulation is the whole essence of the challenge. An added (and perhaps surprising) feature of cryptic crosswords is that the solver usually knows immediately that a solution is correct without needing to relate it to intersecting letters of other solutions. This is because cryptic clues normally contain separate elements within them – and these elements must cross-check to produce a consistent answer.

A cryptic clue always contains a *definition* of the answer to be found together with a 'mysteriously obscure' part which, when solved, also leads to the answer. This latter part is usually referred to as the *subsidiary indication*. The definition normally comes at the beginning or end of a clue, rarely in the middle.

Example: **Bird box on line** (7). 'Bird' is the definition and 'box on line' is the mysteriously obscure part or subsidiary indication. Of course, it's not meant to be obvious when you first look at a clue which part is which: much of the fun is working that out! So, in this example, 'box' = SPAR and 'line' = ROW, so 'box on line' = SPAR on ROW = SPARROW.

The number in brackets at the end of a clue indicates the number of letters in the answer. You may think: 'Why bother to give that information? It's obvious when you look at the diagram'. First of all, it saves you from having to consult the diagram every time; secondly, it is necessary for indicating when an answer comprises more than one word or is a hyphenated word. For example, (3,4) would mean that the answer is two words, the first one 3 letters long, the second one 4 letters long. If it were written (3-4), this would indicate that the word has a hyphen in it after the third letter.

Now for a list of the common clue types and devices. This list is not meant to be exhaustive as there are some clue types and devices used in certain very difficult kinds of cryptic crosswords which, if included here, would make the list too cumbersome and probably frighten the life out of you at this stage! If you cope successfully with the crosswords in this book, then there are other books that will give you an insight into even deeper mysteries of cryptic clues.

The letter introducing each clue type is a reference used in the first two sets of **Graded Puzzles** and also on the bookmark clue type summary. To help you further, the principal **definitional** element in most of the clues has been highlighted, a procedure echoed in the first ten puzzles.

a. Double or multiple definitions
Two or more definitions of the word to be found are chosen so that when they are put together they are misleading.

Examples: **Signify** low average (4) = MEAN

               State proviso (9) = CONDITION

b. Single definition
Although the solution is a single definition, it is not a straightforward or literal definition of the words in the clue.

Example: One who lies quivering at the bottom of the sea? (7,5) = NERVOUS WRECK

(A question mark is sometimes used to emphasize the misleading and perhaps humorous nature of a single definition, as in the above example.)

c. Anagram

i) Simple: The letters of one or more words in the clue are rearranged to form the answer. An anagram indicator also appears somewhere in the clue so that you know that some letters have to be rearranged.

Example: Grab torn **dress** (4) = GARB ('Grab' rearranged)

In this example 'torn' is the anagram indicator. More examples of anagram indicators are given below.

(We have used the term 'simple' to enable us to use the term 'complex' for the other more difficult kinds of anagrams. 'Simple' is not meant to indicate that solving the actual anagram is necessarily easy!)

ii) Complex: The letters of one or more words that do not actually appear in the clue have first of all to be found from a word or words in the clue. These letters then have to be rearranged to form the answer.

Example: Snatch torn **dress** (4) = GARB

The anagram is formed from a synonym of 'snatch' = grab, where 'torn' is again the anagram indicator.

A common variation occurs when part of the anagram is an abbreviation, number or symbol derived from some of the words in the clue.

Example: **Dress** made from black rag (4) = GARB (B + 'rag' rearranged)

In this example 'black' = B, and the anagram indicator is 'made from'.

Examples of anagram indicators:

Anagram indicators are words which indicate the movement or rearrangement of letters, such as: 'flying', 'wild', 'exploding', 'shuffle', 'shake', 'reforming', 'twisted', 'change'. Different tenses of a word may be used, such as: 'change', 'changes', 'changing', 'changed'.

Sometimes, less obvious words are used as anagram indicators, such as: 'fancy', 'out'.

You will realize from this that many words can serve to indicate that the letters of another word or words in the clue are to be rearranged. In solving the puzzles in this book you will probably find that you begin to build up a mental list of some of them. Many are also featured in the **Two-way Crossword Glossary**.

d. Split
The answer is made up of linked parts as in the party game of Charades.

Example: Interrupt quick meal (9) = BREAKFAST (BREAK = 'interrupt' + FAST = 'quick')

e. Sandwich
One component of the answer is expressed as, for example, being 'in' or 'around' another.

Example: **Widest** and best way in (8) = BROADEST

ROAD = 'way' and this goes in the word BEST.

f. Takeaway sandwich
In this case, part of the 'filling' of a 'sandwich' is taken away to give the answer, either from words featured in the clue or from synonyms of them.

Example: Stayed topless and **hurried**! (4) = SPED

'Stayed' = StopPED less 'top'.

g. Reverse direction, either horizontal or vertical
A word or words must be written either back-to-front in an Across clue, or from bottom to top in a Down clue. The word or words indicating this process usually correspond with the clue direction. For Across clues, the indicator may be, for example, 'returning', or 'back', while for a Down clue it could be 'rising' or 'falling', 'uplifting', or simply 'up' or 'down'.

Example: Keep turning round **to take a sly look** (4) = PEEK ('Keep' reversed)

h. Hidden word
The answer is found in the wording of the clue, and a word such as 'some' or 'part' or 'in' is used to indicate that this is so.

Example: **Try** some white streamers (4) = TEST ('whiTE STreamers')

i.   Sound effects
The solution is usually a synonym of one of the elements in the clue and a homophone of (that is, sounds like) another. Indicators of this may be, for example, 'we hear', 'sounds like', 'said', 'reported'.

Example: **Animal** sounds husky (5) = HORSE (sounds like 'hoarse')

j.   Takeaway
Part of a word is taken away, leaving the answer, rather as in **f.** above.

Example: **Design** flying machine with no tail (4) = PLAN ('flying machine' = PLANE minus E)

k. Moving letter
One or more letters are directed to another position in the word.

Example: **Look**: Pepe's swallowing his tail (4) = PEEP (final 'e' from 'Pepe')

l.   Substituted letter
One letter of a word in the clue takes the place of another, and there will be a word or phrase indicating that this is so.

Example: **Value** change of direction from North (5) = WORTH

'Direction' in this clue indicates a compass direction (the solver has to discover this), so the N = 'North' changes to W = 'West'. Although 'Value' in the clue is read as a verb, this is meant to mislead: the definition requires 'value' to be regarded as a noun.

m. Alternate letters
The answer is produced from alternate letters in part of the clue. The indicator for this type may be, for example, 'evenly', 'unevenly', 'oddly', 'every other'.

Example: **Liquid** found in every other gorilla (3) = OIL ('gOrIlLa')

n. Letter positions
i)   Initials or last letters only: The first or last letters of the indicated words are taken to produce the answer.

The indicator for the first letters may be, for example, 'firstly', 'first of all', 'initially', 'heads of', 'tops of'.

Example: First of all men, often use new tackle to **climb** (5) = MOUNT

Take the first letters of 'Men Often Use New Tackle'.

The indicator for the last letters may be, for example, 'ends of', 'lastly', 'last of all'.

Example: Last of all, feed the little river **animal**. (4) = DEER

Take the last letters of 'feeD thE littlE riveR'.

ii) **Only specifically placed letters**: Letters in certain positions in indicated words are taken to produce part or, in a few cases, the whole of the answer.

The indicator for the first letter of a word may be similar to those in **n. i)**, except indicators in the plural would become singular: 'head of', 'top of'. Also, a word with 'head' or 'top' at the end would indicate that the first letter of that word is to be taken; for example: 'Gateshead' = G, or 'worktop' = W.

The indicator for the middle letter of a word may be, typically, 'centre of', 'middle of', 'heart of', 'centre'. So, 'Middle of Glasgow' would be S.

The indicator for the last letter of a word might be, perhaps, 'end of', 'lastly', 'tail of'. So, 'end of sermon' would be N. Also, a word with 'end' or 'tail' at the end would indicate that the last letter of the word before 'end' or 'tail' is to be taken; for example: 'fantail' would be N.

The indicator for other positions could be simply 'second', 'third', 'fourth' and so on, indicating that the second, third or fourth letter of the word indicated is to be taken; for example: 'third of January' is N.

Examples of some of the above:

> **Mist** in the centre of Oxford and Gateshead. (3) = FOG

FO = centre of 'Oxford', G = 'Gateshead'

o. Abbreviations, numbers and symbols

Abbreviations are often used to indicate one or more letters in a solution.

Example: **A mass meeting** of everyone in the railway (5) = RALLY

'Everyone' = ALL in RY – which is an abbreviation of 'railway' or 'railway line'. Sometimes just the word 'line' is used to indicate the abbreviation RY.

Some dictionaries carry a list of common abbreviations, and a look through these will show that there is plenty of scope for their use in clues. As you work through the crosswords in this book, you will gradually become familiar with many of them. Some of the more common ones, however, are worth mentioning here.

Let's start off with the points of the compass: North, South, East and West are often abbreviated to N, S, E and W respectively. In clues these are often referred to as 'points', 'quarters' or 'directions' – the latter quite possibly also being NE, SE, SW and so on. Other geographical references may well include the abbreviations of countries (US or USA and all its states – CA, PA, NY, for example) or features such as 'river' (R), 'mountain' (MT) and 'lake' (L).

Moving from places to people, we often encounter professions and qualifications such as DR, GP or MB ('doctor'), DA ('American lawyer', or just 'lawyer'), RA ('painter'), REV ('vicar', 'priest' or 'churchman'), MP, LIB, LAB, C, TORY ('Member' or 'politician') and BA or MA ('graduate'). A 'learner', by the way, is nearly always L and a 'saint' or 'good man' ST.

Abbreviations relating to the armed forces are also very common. The favourites are probably TA ('army', 'reserves' or 'volunteers'), RA ('gunners' or 'artillery'), RE ('engineers' or 'sappers') and GI (frequently just 'soldier'). The 'navy' (RN) seems to recruit mainly ABs ('sailors' when they are not TARS) and the occasional RM (very often a 'jolly' fellow) to sail aboard its 'ships' (SS), while the airforce (RAF) has a full complement of ACS (usually 'airmen'). Every AC will pay wages into a 'current' (AC or DC) 'account' (again AC), of course.

Military personnel are commanded by a variety of 'officers' – both commissioned (CO) and non-commissioned (NCO) – ranging from GEN through COL, LT and CAPT to SGT, but often referred to simply as 'commanding officer' (CO) or the person 'in charge' (IC). At the head of the armed forces is the monarch – the 'king' or 'queen' – who may well be a George (GR), an Elizabeth (ER, sometimes 'the First' – ERI) or simply an R, and who receives religious sanction from the 'Church' (CE or CH).

After the fighting is over, one of the principal forms of relaxation is cricket, in which 'runs'(R) are scored, often as 'extras' (LB or leg-byes), on both 'sides' of the (W) 'wicket' – OFF and ON/LEG, though these are not really abbreviations. In cricket, if you are not 'batting' (IN), you are out, and this can happen in a number of ways: 'caught' (C) is the most common, although many players are 'bowled' (B) and some can even be 'stumped' (ST). Golf, tennis, rowing, football (run by the FA, of course), rugby (RU) and bridge (for which 'partners', N,S,E,W are required) are other pastimes much favoured in crosswords. Team games are mostly played by an 'eleven' (XI) or a 'fifteen' (XV); however, these belong to the realm of 'numbers' (NOS).

Not surprisingly, Roman numerals are a staple feature of cryptic crosswords. Just to remind you: I = 'one', IV = 'four', V = 'five', IX = 'nine', X = 'ten', L = 'fifty', C = 'hundred' (and is also an abbreviation for *circa* meaning 'about'), D = 'five hundred' and M = 'thousand'. Perhaps the most common number in crosswords is O, which can be indicated by 'zero', 'nought', 'none', 'no', 'nothing' and, quite often, by 'love' – a reference to tennis scoring.

Strictly speaking, of course, numbers are symbols rather than abbreviations. Other symbols to be 'noted' are A,B,C,D,E,F,G – musical notes, which can also crop up as DO(H), RE/RAY, MI/ME and so on. Symbols for chemical 'elements' are not uncommon, such as K (Potassium), NA (Sodium) and S (Sulphur). X is indicated in a variety of ways: as well as being the number 'ten', it is also a 'kiss', a 'cross', and an 'unknown quantity'(for which Y may also serve).

These are just a few of the many building blocks for 'structural' clues. The **Two-way Crossword Glossary** features many more examples for reference when you start doing the puzzles.

p. Misleading punctuation

i) **Misleading marks or absence of them**: An example of this would be the use of the word 'Gateshead' in a clue to indicate G, (see **n.ii**). 'Gates' should really have an apostrophe thus: 'Gate's'.

ii) **Running words together or falsely separating them**: (This also includes the running together or separation of a word and a letter. Using the same example as in **p.i**), 'Gateshead' should be two words: 'Gate's head', or in the clue: '**Horse**men often use new tackle at first (5)', where the answer is MOUNT, the clue should read '**Horse** men ...'

iii) **False upper or lower case letters**: Again, we can use 'Gateshead' as an example: literally, it should be 'gate's head'. In **k.** above, 'Pepe's' should be 'pepe's'.

q. Literary, historical or artistic references
Where literature is involved, references are sometimes used in preference to direct quotations.

Examples: The less dignified end of one of Shakespeare's plays? (6) = BOTTOM

The Bard's small village? (6) = HAMLET

Constable's transport? (3,3,4) = THE HAY WAIN

The question mark is used to indicate the 'tongue-in-cheek' nature of these clues.

Where direct quotations are used, setters usually try to ensure that they are either well known or that they can be reasonably easily deduced from their context.

Example: 'Cry, — , and let slip the dogs of war' (*Julius Caesar*) (5) = HAVOC

r. Direct or indirect reference to another clue in the puzzle, or its answer
This may be expressed in the form: 7 *Dn*'s muddled thought. (4) = IDEA, where the answer to the seven down clue is AIDE.

s. Archaic indicator
Sometimes a setter will use a word which is no longer in common usage or an obsolete meaning of an everyday word, and it is only fair to solvers that this should be indicated in some way in the clue. Examples of these indicators are: 'ancient', 'old', 'was', 'Shakespearian', 'Spenser's'.

Example: Old penny has changed to **Mark**. (4) = DASH
                    (D + 'has' anagram)

In this example, an 'old penny' is indicated by the symbol D (now largely obsolete) and 'Mark' is misleadingly printed with upper-case 'M'.

t. Miscellaneous
Sometimes a clue, or part of a clue, doesn't fit into any of the above types.

Example: **A tiny particle** in a,b,c,d,e,f,g,h,i,j,k,l,m (4) = ATOM (A TO M)

All such clues are explained in the **Help** section.

u. Definition also being a part of, or the whole of, the device
At the beginning of this section of the book we wrote about cryptic clues containing a definition and a subsidiary indication. We now come to the type of clue where either the definition is included in part of the subsidiary indication, or the subsidiary indication is also the definition.

Example: **Broken** tubs (4) = BUST

Here, 'broken' is both the definition and the anagram indicator.

Example: **Heads of** the several amalgamated **Russian States** (5)
                    = TSARS

In this case, despite the bold type, the whole clue is effectively both the definition and the subsidiary indication. This is what is known as a true '& lit.' clue, which means that it offers a subsidiary indication (in this case of the type **n.i** above) and a literal definition, both of which use all the words in the clue.

Connectors

Finally, we need to mention that a word or words are often inserted in a clue which help connect the definition with the subsidiary indication, but which are part of neither. They may also be inserted to help the clue to make sense or read well.

Example: **Dispatch** in Southend (4) = SEND

'Dispatch' is the definition, and 'Southend' is the subsidiary indication. The connector 'in' serves both to give the clue a coherent literal meaning and to indicate the derivation of the definition from the sudsidiary indication.

Some Practical Advice on Solving

Before you start trying to solve the crosswords in this book, just take the time to read this short section. It will give you some useful pointers to various strategies you can employ when tackling a crossword, as well as a brief run-down on the puzzles you will find in a few of the national dailies.

Some of what follows may strike you as a trifle obvious; or it might appear a rather tendentious way of approaching what should be an enjoyable pastime. However, if you are a real beginner at cryptic crosswords, you could well benefit from the practical advice offered here – firstly to establish a sound technique, and secondly to prevent you getting overwhelmed or dispirited when you gaze at a blank grid and a lot of seemingly bizarre clues.

In many ways (and don't let this put you off), one or two of the techniques for starting to solve crosswords can be likened to those used when taking an exam – though, of course, there's no time limit and nobody is going to shout at you if you fail! The most important piece of advice is to read through all the clues in order (Across, then Down) before you begin filling in the grid. There is nothing more irritating than struggling over, say, an Across clue when there are one or two easy intersecting Down clues that could have helped you to solve it had you only taken the trouble to look.

During this quick evaluation process, you should be concentrating on isolating the definitional element of each clue. Once you have done this, most types of clue become much more accessible. You should also be on the lookout for hidden word and anagram devices: clues containing these are usually the easiest to solve. When you find such clues, ring round the number so you can go back to them later – you're already halfway there with the solution. While you are reading the clues, you can also tick (or otherwise mark) any that you think you have solved correctly.

Having gone through the clues in this way – which shouldn't take you more than about five minutes – use a pencil (or a pen, if you are feeling confident) to write in those solutions you have worked out. Then set about unscrambling the anagrams you have identified.

Most solvers find it easiest to do anagrams by separating out the consonants and vowels of the constituent word or words. When written down in this way, the individual letters can be more easily dissociated in the mind from the form of the original clue so that attention can be focused on the various potential letter combinations of the solution indicated. It is often helpful to identify any possible consonant clusters or obvious sequences of letters (such as CH, CK, PH, QU, SH, TH, CL, THR and so on) that might form part of the rearranged solution. It is also important to relate the tense or number implied by the clue indicator to the letters in the anagram. For example, in 'Staple used to form folds (6)', the word 'folds' indicates a plural answer is to be sought (PLEATS). Or in 'Fed up by getting dates wrong (5)', where a past tense is implied by 'Fed', you can begin by working out words that can be formed with the ending -ED. (The answer is, of course, SATED.) All this being said, you must still bear in mind that the plurals of many Latinate terms end in -I (especially those of plants) and that certain strong verbs in English have past forms ending in -T or -N (THOUGHT and RIDDEN for example), so don't allow your mind to shut out these possibilities. Other useful endings to look for are -ION , -ITY and -UDE (abstract nouns), -ER and -OR (often common nouns or 'agents'), -ING (verbs and verbal nouns) and -ABLE, -IBLE, -UBLE or -IOUS, -OUS (adjectives). Prefixes such as ANTE-, ANTI-, BE-, CON-, DE-, DIS-, FOR-, IN-, MIS-, RE- and UN- are also useful starting points. Finally (though there is a lot more we could say about anagrams), the letter Y is a semi-vowel, and some solvers write it down separately above the line of constituent vowels in their anagram letter listing. Y can often be used to form an adjective (PRETTY) but it just as frequently functions as a vowel on its own (SKY) or a letter modifying the sound of a preceding vowel (TRAY, GREY and so on).

Back to the puzzle! Having solved one or two of the anagrams means that you will have got some letters of the intersecting answers (or 'lights' as they are sometimes termed). These 'check squares' will provide you with a much better basis on which to go back and review the other clues. Although that may sound rather trite, it is important to realize that many of the clues in cryptic crosswords contain 'structural' devices – such as the abbreviation of directions (N, E, S, W) – which are part of the final solution. To have established a little of the content of a light through a check letter can therefore be even more useful in a cryptic crossword than in an ordinary definitional puzzle: the letter you have got may often represent a key pointer towards the construction of the clue.

Which clues should you concentrate on? Once again, this may sound glaringly evident, but it's always best at the beginning to try and get the longer solutions since their component letters are clearly going to be helpful in solving the other clues – for the reason indicated above. Depending on the shape of the grid, try working on one corner or area of the puzzle at a time: the more clues you solve, the easier the others will become. This is not merely because of the insights provided by the intersecting letters: it is also a function of getting to know a particular setter's mind, style and personal enthusiasms.

Make sure, however, that you don't get obsessed at an early stage with individual clues: there's plenty of time for that later! If your brain begins to overheat, go and have a look at another clue – or try doing a different area of the puzzle. One of the great things about crosswords of all varieties is that your mind is always subconsciously working on associations and ideas, even while you are apparently concentrating on something else. You will often be surprised to find that a clue you previously thought was completely opaque suddenly appears blindingly obvious when you come back to it after a short break.

This is particularly true when you are at an early stage of learning how to do cryptic crosswords, largely because much of the learning process involves becoming attuned to the different kinds of ambiguity encountered in the clues. People who don't do cryptic crosswords often complain that they read like a foreign language – and we would be lying if we did not confess that there is an element of truth in this. However, learning to understand the language of crosswords is much easier than learning a foreign language because crosswords use terms that we are all familiar with. So in some ways it's really more like cracking a code – a code in which, for example, a graduate is almost invariably an MA or BA, a bridge is often a SPANNER and a duck or love is usually O. We have tried to list some of the more common ambiguities (mostly abbreviations and symbols) in the **Two-way Crossword Glossary**. However, there are literally thousands of potential ways of wrong-footing the solver and, taking the language-learning parallel again, it is a matter of becoming used to thinking in the language rather than learning every word of it by heart. Best expressed, the trick is to think laterally but always logically.

Pursuing this theme a little further, let us just look for a moment at word order. It is vital that you do not allow the apparently innocent literal meaning of a clue to influence your judgement about the solution indicated. In many ways, this is probably a bigger hurdle for the novice than the matter of learning to cope with the abbreviations, symbols and vocabulary of cryptic puzzles. You really need to approach each clue by thinking of ways in which the natural syntax could be disrupted. Take, for example, a clue from a typical *Times* crossword: 'Doctor calls back after 45 minutes (8)'. In this clue, 'calls' is NAMES, which spelt backwards is SEMAN. This must be put 'after' three-quarters of an hour – HOU ('45 minutes') – giving you HOUSEMAN, the 'doctor' indicated at the start of the clue. Thus, in order to solve that particular clue, you would need to read it as '**Doctor** | calls back(wards) | after 45 minutes'. You can see from this that even the word 'after' contains a possible ambiguity since your first thought might well have been that the '45 minutes' element should actually follow 'calls back'. This is not to mention the fact that we have already made the assumption that 'Doctor' is a noun: it could quite easily have been a verb! The point is, therefore, that you must be prepared to dissect each clue and examine every word in order to reach the correct solution.

Of course, not all clues are of the structural type: many depend simply on puns and *double entendres*. These clues are often the most amusing and the most satisfying to solve, although they are often the most difficult because there is no way of building up the answer. Once again, a typical example from a *Times* crossword: 'Europeans who go to Rome for religious service (5,5)'. Apart from the implication that the solution has a plural ending, this clue depends entirely on a misreading of 'service'; once you have figured out that the connotation is a military one, the solution (SWISS GUARD) is fairly obvious. The lateral jump of the imagination needed to make this connection is what solving cryptic crosswords is all about, and to learn to think in this way takes time and practice – so don't be put off if you can't solve this sort of clue quickly: you often need to have quite a few intersecting letters before the answer becomes obvious and the pun dawns on you. It's almost a question of needing to have the solution in order to understand the clue!

In this respect, you should not be afraid of the occasional piece of inspired guesswork. Sometimes the check letters dictate that a particular solution is almost inevitable, and it is only after you have written it down that you make the connection. Even so, you are strongly advised not to ink in a solution until you are absolutely sure that you have understood why it is correct. An incorrect or hasty assumption can hold you up for an awful long time – so it is wiser just to trace the letters of a 'best guess' on any blank check squares rather than write in the whole word or phrase. Apart from anything else, writing in a suspicion that proves to be wrong makes it extremely difficult to concentrate on getting the right answer after you have realized your mistake.

Another useful point to bear in mind is that most normal puzzles will contain a fairly even balance of the different types of clue device, carefully distributed throughout the grid. In other words, there will be several anagrams, a number of structural clues, a few puns, no more than one or two hidden words and 'initial letter' clues, and perhaps a quotation. All of these will be mixed into the sequence of clues so that you are unlikely to encounter a large number of consecutive clues of the same type. This factor can be particularly useful if you are stuck on a certain clue: it is quite possible that it will feature a different device from the ones immediately preceding and following it.

Of course, different setters favour different types of clue and so the overall balance can be different from puzzle to puzzle. It is also possible for personal enthusiasms to manifest themselves within both the clues and solutions: gardening, cricket, bridge and certain periods of literature are particularly common. Some crosswords are even deliberately constructed with particular themes or leitmotifs in mind – though this is usually made explicit in an accompanying rubric. Despite the balance and variation of clue types, however, it is probably fair to say that each of the major dailies has a certain style that characterizes most of the crosswords that appear in it. The truth of this may be judged from the fact that once you have become used to solving puzzles in one paper, it can take you a while to get to grips with the puzzles in another – even though the level of difficulty may be similar, or perhaps even lower.

Our own experience does not allow any detailed comment on the puzzles that appear in the *Scotsman* (which has an excellent crossword) or in the *Irish Times*. However, you might be interested in a thumbnail sketch of some of the ones we are more familiar with personally in order to plan your future newspaper order.

The *Financial Times* features a daily cryptic of medium difficulty. The clues are enjoyable, though they rarely reach the level of being abstruse or inspired. A quotation or two is generally included. The *FT* crossword is an excellent proposition for the relative beginner or the casual solver: satisfying without being too demanding. To come to the *FT* after any other paper is a disorientating experience unless you are accustomed to writing on pink stationery.

The Guardian has an interesting (though sometimes complex) crossword that often contains up-to-the-minute allusions and consistently features extensive cross-references between clues. Unlike the other daily paper puzzles, *Guardian* crosswords are set by named compilers – or, more accurately, by compilers with their own pseudonyms – so after a while, solving a Custos or Fidelio or Araucaria can almost be like renewing a relationship with an old friend or, some might say, doing battle with an old enemy. The practical advantage of a system of named compilers is that you can frequently anticipate when a puzzle is going to be easy or difficult (no names, no pack-drill!) rather than taking pot luck with an anonymous puzzle.

The *Independent* features a challenging crossword, which is in style, content and general level of difficulty similar to the *Times*. The allusions and references in the *Independent* crossword are frequently bolder and more contemporary than those in the *Times* – perhaps reflecting the younger profile of the paper's readership.

The *Telegraph* crossword is probably the classic cryptic and is a great puzzle for beginners. Though the level of difficulty varies from day to day (as is the case with all of the national papers), the *Telegraph* is always enjoyable and is particularly good for building up a knowledge of the abbreviations, symbols and syntax needed to solve structural clues. It is probably fair to say that the references and allusions in *Telegraph* crosswords are not generally as racy as those in *Guardian* or *Independent* puzzles but the clues are in many ways more accessible to the novice solver. All in all, the *Telegraph* crossword is to be heartily recommended as an excellent precursor to more advanced solving.

This brings us on to the crossword that most fanatics see as the ultimate daily challenge, the *Times*. As a matter of fact, the *Times* is not really the sole province of Whitehall boffins and winners of *Mastermind* – the image that it seems to conjure up for people who don't solve crosswords. It is closely monitored and edited for level of difficulty, and the current Crossword Editor John Grant works hard to ensure that neither the clues nor the solutions contain any vocabulary or allusions so abstruse as to require more than the occasional reference to a good desk dictionary. Even the quotation type of clue, which appears perhaps more frequently in the *Times* than in most other crosswords, is usually well-known or reasonably easy to deduce from the context once you have a few of the intersecting letters of the solution. What makes the *Times* good is the consistently high quality of syntax and originality in the clues: it is rare that even on a Monday (usually the easiest day) there are not at least one or two that bring a quiet glow of inner satisfaction when solved.

Part of the reputation of the *Times* in recent years rests on the fact that it runs an annual National Crossword Championship, which has become extremely popular among solvers of all ages everywhere. For many years the undefeated champion was Dr John Sykes, the Oxford University Press lexicographer. Dr Sykes is famous for his accuracy and unsurpassed breadth of knowledge in solving crosswords, rather than for his pure speed. One of the most famous speed solvers of bygone days, appparently, was the Provost of Eton, who was reputed to be able to solve the *Times* crossword while boiling his breakfast egg. It used to be said that he liked his eggs but not his crosswords hard!

Apart from the *Times* championship, most national papers run a prize crossword on Saturdays. Unlike the Championship, these crosswords do not involve a trial against the clock, and though the puzzles are usually a little tougher than those appearing on weekdays, they are great fun to solve and send in – even if the chances of winning are not exactly guaranteed! Michael Mates, the Conservative MP, once held a party in the House of Commons to celebrate having won his first *Times* crossword competition after sending in completed puzzles for almost twenty years.

No doubt Mr Mates enjoyed solving every one of those prize puzzles plus all the other crosswords that he has almost certainly attempted and completed during those years. Whether you are tackling the *Mail* or *Express* (both of which have very enjoyable cryptics) or the real mindbenders in the weekend colour supplements (after you've disposed of the ones in the main papers, of course), you will be one of a growing number who have discovered the joys of the cryptic crosswords – a truly stimulating and rewarding intellectual pastime, and yours for the price of a paper.

Crosswords 1 - 10

The first ten puzzles are reasonably easy. The clues are representative of the sort of standard you might find in a cryptic such as the *Daily Mail*, *Daily Express* or occasionally in the *Telegraph*. The clues do not contain any particularly obscure terms and the solutions should not require the use of a dictionary. There is a progression of difficulty from one puzzle to the next which has been established through averaging out the time taken to solve each one by a number of a solvers of varying levels of experience.

The first ten puzzles contain a square-bracketed indication against each clue of the type of device being used. This is keyed to the explanations in the section **Cryptic Clue Types and Devices**, a summary of which is also available on the bookmark for ease of reference. By and large, the order of listing of the indications is designed to give an idea of the way that the elements in each clue build up to form the solution. However, the indications are intended to function as a helpful pointer to the *type* of clue being looked at, rather than as an exhaustive dissection of every single element in the clue. Thus, for instance, where a clue contains more than one abbreviation, there is not an individual annotation for each abbreviation (except in a few more complex examples) as this would have looked cumbersome and could have become confusing. Neither have we indicated every instance of misleading punctuation, preferring to highlight those that seemed especially deceptive, or which caused our novice solvers particular problems.

As a further aid to beginners, we have also highlighted the definitional element of the clues (single definitions and quotation-based clues excepted for obvious reasons) in **bold** type. This is to allow solvers to concentrate on how the various devices work – which is particularly important in the early stages of learning how to do cryptic crosswords. In the case of double or multiple definition clues, we have tried to highlight the literal or least misleading definition.

Finally, we have provided a head start in these early puzzles by filling in some of the solutions on the grids. The clues chosen for completion were selected either as being of more than usual difficulty or as being structurally helpful for solving and checking other tougher clues on the grid.

When solving the puzzles, remember that the **Two-way Crossword Glossary** contains a lot of useful information and that the **Help** section explains many of the solutions in detail.

Across

4   Second coach **used to make tea** (8) [o,d]
8   **Cutlery** awarded as second prize? (6) [a]
9   **Come into view again** to cut down fruit (8) [d]
10 Period of time following brief **deficit** (8) [d]
11 **Robbery** causes delay? (4,2) [a]
12 If machine goes wrong, first call **this person to fix it!** (8) [cii,nii]
13 Survival from past drinking bout? (8) [b]
16 **Confrontation** after demonstration put down (8) [d]
19 If you go to these, you may have gone too far (8) [b]
21 **Believe in** borrowing money (6) [a]
23 Perhaps the function of 1? (8) [b,r]
24 Nice oils could be used to make this **kind of polish** (8) [ci]
25 Embittered, Ralph holds up **store** (6) [h,g]
26 Saw knees wobble showing **lack of strength** (8) [ci]

Down

1   Boat that's **not so heavy** (6) [a]
2   **Ruin** chance of extra run (9) [a]
3   Appoint – to holy orders? (6) [b]
4   Have a bit of exercise and become taller? (7,4,4) [b]
5   **Managing to touch** everyone separately in circle (8) [e]
6   **Urge forward** politician involved in awful lie (5) [o,e,cii]
7   **Rubbing out** is certain following initial error by artist (7) [d,nii,o]
14 Present conservative **collection** (9) [d,o]
15 American zip? (8) [b]
17 Drug to end life of **brave woman** (7) [d,nii]
18 Lacking direction, **wander** with me instead! (7) [l,u]
20 Got up with bad leg attached to **kind of fastener** (6) [g,d,ci]
22 **Swallow**tails from Hyderabad, Kashmir, Delhi, Rangoon and Bangkok (5) [pii,ni]

1

Across

1 It's amusing **having people for a meal** (12) [a]

9 **Exaggerate** concerning condition (9) [d]

10 **Sluggish** trainer tries to take part (5) [h]

11 **Design** fashionable camping equipment (6) [d]

12 Tree taken to servant for **civic dignitary** (8) [d]

13 Initially galloping round **the field** (6) [nii,d]

15 **Designated** as indicated (8) [d]

18 Trick to test **scorn** (8) [d]

19 Everyone gets holy men round for **church-seats** (6) [e,o]

21 **Implement for training** silent ringer? (4,4) [d]

23 A tissue, we hear, might be appropriate for this **sudden attack**! (6) [i]

26 Heather, love, **this language is not understood** (5) [d,o]

27 **The head of a council** is a person initially dwelling in a place for some time (9) [nii,d]

28 **Someone trying to be like another** man, so I report in a confused way (12) [ci]

Down

1 Wearing rigout done with style (7) [pii,cii]

2 **Pay for someone** to negotiate (5) [a]

3 Cranes one engineered produce **sympathetic vibration** (9) [ci]

4 A girl is heard to make **an expression of grief** (4) [i,d]

5 Irritates skinhead – it's **unnecessary** (8) [d,nii,pii]

6 There's a **din** in here when the volcano is erupting (5) [h]

7 End **part of plug**? (8) [a]

8 Newspaperman following point-to-point is **very drunk** (6) [o,o,d]

14 **Adorn** or designate part of the Bible (8) [d,o]

16 11 and one on **purpose** (9) [r,o,d]

17 **A dessert** order that is perfect (5,3) [a]

18 **Pamper** old king who embraces learned religious person (6) [q,e,o]

20 Very thin lieutenant squeezes into **harbour** (7) [e,o]

22 **Brush** bedroom when little Edward has left (5) [f,o]

24 **Choose** from very delectable fruits (5) [h]

25 Immerses every other one in **confusion** (4) [m]

2

Across

1   Russian vehicle **not far from Middlesbrough** (6) [d]
4   Keeps company with royalty? (8) [b]
9   Bit of magic performed on deck? (4,5) [b]
11 **The man** Merle is nuts about? (5) [ci]
12 Is he a farmer holding a **harvest bundle**? (5) [h]
13 Sounds like selling the **joy of cycling**! 9) [i]
15 **Born** in need (3) [h]
17 **Puzzling diversion** using lights (9) [b]
20 **Frightened** to make a mistake if in raging tide (9) [e,cii]
21 Desert **animal** (3) [a]
23 Verse points to **Chinese dialect** (9) [d,o]
25 Strange graduate at **dance** (5) [d,o]
27 Some mechanised **plant** (5) [h]
28 Draw on garbled rot included in **preface** (9) [e,cii]
29 Terns go South in error – but not this **bird** (8) [cii,o]
30 Girl inside points to **fish** (6) [e,o]

Down

1   Doubtless unsuitable as a lullaby! (4,4) [b]
2   Hymn for one who is late? (5) [b]
3   **Craftsman** with a terrific innovation ((9) [ci]
5   All right round a **wood** (3) [o,e]
6   **A period** of enchantment (5) [a]
7   Sell off cheaply **what's left** (9) [a]
8   **Signals indifference** to second-hand carpets (6) [o,d]
10 **To make it up on the spot** is better all round (9) [e]
14 Disagreement in which I'd be **a protestor** (9) [e]
16 **Added piece** is stretching it a bit! (9) [a]
18 Does the salesman open this under strict instruction? (5,4) [b]
19 Common cold's treated by a river outing on one of these **boats** (8) [f]
22 **What pets may be given** to fight sickness initially (6) [d,nii]
24 Gangs of witches caught leaving **heated chambers** (5) [j]
26 **Climb upon** poetic steed (5) [a]
28 Even filches **diamonds** (3) [m]

3

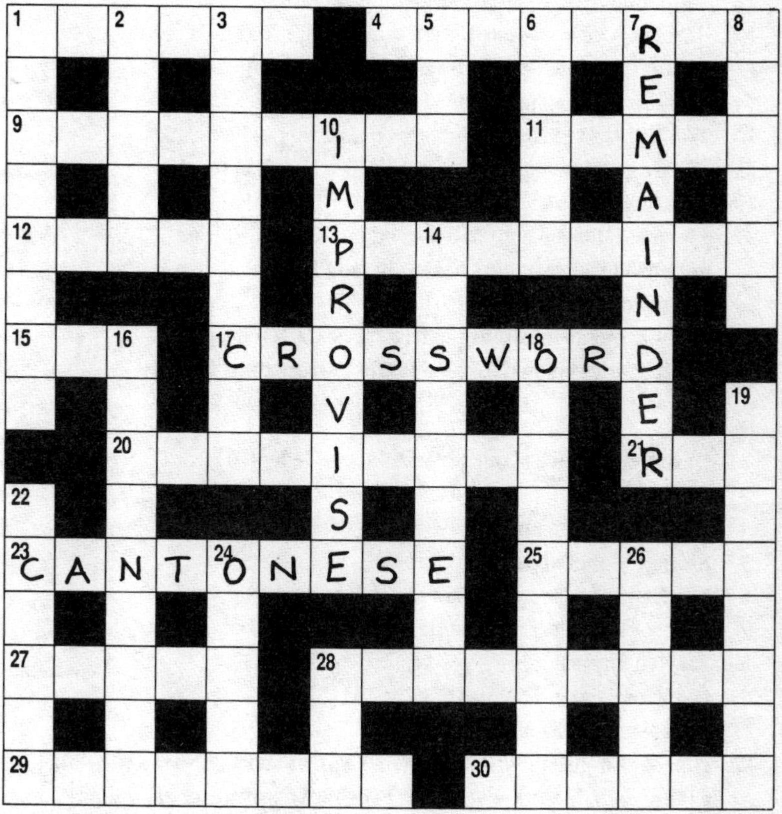
REMAINDER
IMPROVISE
CROSSWORD
CANTONESE

Across

1 Security-conscious astronomer? (5,8) [b]

10 Bite not as bad **as a mule** (9) [ci]

11 Peril almost causes **great annoyance** (5) [j]

12 Bird takes very last **position in field** (5) [d,nii]

13 **Laziness** in new church about grief (9) [d,o,o,e]

14 **Time** for making uniform? (7) [a]

16 'This blessed plot, this earth, this realm, this —' *(Richard II)* (7) [q]

18 **Soaking** bad twinge? It's about the first time! (7) [cii,nii]

20 To match **completely** (7) [d]

21 **Elevate** damaged automobiles without wheels (9) [cii,j]

23 Sounds like a way to get **heavenly food** (5) [i]

24 Former deed is **accurate** (5) [d]

25 A tragic member resolved to be **practical** (9) [cii,o]

26 To trick after going down is **awfully patronizing** (13) [d]

Down

2 **Bankrupt** is rude about advocate's third letter (9) [e,nii]

3 Bald men aren't **dangerous**! (5) [a]

4 **Displaying** organ in part of building (7) [e]

5 Strangely altered **pedal** (7) [ci]

6 Car fixture might be a bright idea for miners (9) [b]

7 **Gas** container is near gondola (5) [h]

8 Latvian tormentor? **It's hard to say** (6,7) [d]

9 Game played on Tongan Island? (8,5) [b]

15 **Began** to instruct leading driver (9) [d,nii]

17 Head of English town disappeared to **somewhere in North Virginia** (9) [j]

19 Lightweight Manx cat after **this overblown swimmer** (7) [pii,j,d]

20 Mostly generate change **between twelve and twenty** (7) [j,cii]

22 British eggs sent up **well done** (5) [o,g,d]

23 Took part in a play where actions speak louder than words (5) [b]

4

Across

1   **Shrewd** as tutee but missing point (6) [j,o]
4   River **plant** (6) [a]
9   Dig up acre to grow **maple** (4) [ci]
10 **Eminence** of Conservative following concert in progress (10) [o,d]
11 Disapproval expressed when finding a doctor in the **grass** (6) [e,o]
12 Fairly often combined with this, paradoxically, when roundly beaten (8) [b]
13 With 'shining morning face', Shakespeare's crept 'like snail unwillingly' (9) [q]
15 **Drama** children may enjoy (4) [a]
16 Stop breaking **jars**! (4) [ci]
17 A lame bird's recovery is **highly appreciated** (9) [ci]
21 Note Queen Elizabeth I twice got this **tropical disease** (8) [o,d,o]
22 **Fail** to work on the farm (6) [a]
24 Heroine discovered Operation Red Nell was covered up by C.I.A. (10) [cii]
25 Initially night owls often nap at this **time of day** (4) [ni]
26 **Important dramatic character** sounds as though he is sincere in this (6) [a,i]
27 Master arranged **division of pupils according to ability** (6) [ci]

Down

1   Could one really describe Noah's vessel as this **old-fashioned**? (7) [b,i]
2   **Soundly beat** some towpath robbers (5) [h]
3   Oil spot ruined **surface material** (7) [ci]
5   Visit old friend, possibly, **to consult a reference book** (4,2) [a]
6   **Hairy swimmer** responsible for a fleet war breaking out (5-4) [ci]
7   Rugby Union rally **out of town**? (7) [o,d]
8   Around West Beds, ancient uplands are **a famous beauty spot** (8,5) [o,piii,d]
14 **Beaten** duke routed in disorder (9) [o,cii]
16 **Proposition** before young lady is announced (7) [d,i]
18 Lift motorway plant for **operation** (7) [g,o,d]
19 **Space to stretch out** for the French husband? (7) [d]
20 **Red cards** from the art shop (6) [h]
23 Lightweight **cat**? (5) [pii,a]

5

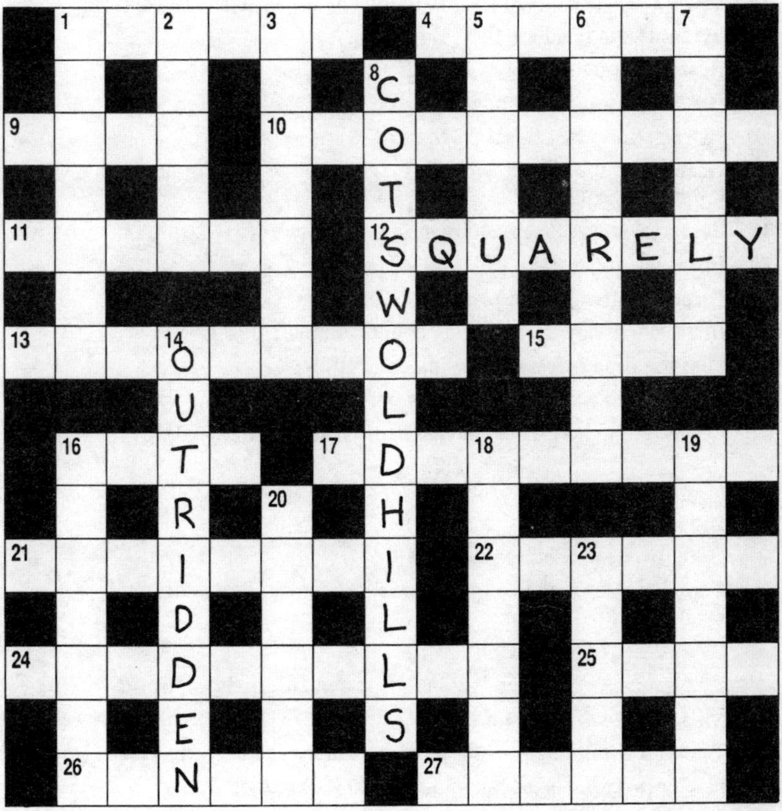
COTSWOLDHILLS
SQUARELY
OUTRIDDEN

Across

1   **Old** type of novel (10) [a]

8   **Ascetic** bear! (4) [a]

10 **Brown** describes Wandsworth or Greenham, for instance (6,4) [a]

11 **Stream** with headless fish (4) [j]

13 Reveals mystery to **a few** (7) [ci]

15 Hush rude sound! It's **acute** (6) [d,i]

16 Head gunner becomes right **coward** (6) [l]

17 Grave need made East Australian first turn into **leading lady!** (4,4,7) [cii,o,ni]

18 Prepare food that is **eaten by many Americans** (6) [d,o]

20 Fixed leg and made it **crooked** (6) [ci]

21 Directions to police **to prosecute** (7) [o,d]

22 In back-tracking union I bring about **collapse** (4) [o,g,e]

25 Dim intuition is **lessening** without it (10) [j]

26 **Situation** in which Shiite throws out greeting (4) [j]

27 Does signing here imply having **broken** some **rule**? (6,4) [b]

Down

2   **Indian** from Brahmin caste (4) [h]

3   Herb, we hear, used to **season** (4) [i]

4   Tortuous detour, with a roundabout replacing a turn, is **firmly established** (6) [cii,l]

5   **Greenkeeper?** (15) [a,pii]

6   Lying upon my back and rubbing first parts **of the lower spine** (6) [ni]

7   Miss China with **constant companion** (10) [d]

9   Team up with football club starting off **in an easterly direction** (10) [d]

12 Doctor in Troon is the top **wind player** (10) [o,e,d,nii]

13 Affectionate reference to a child **may be humbug!** (7) [a]

14 **Plant** that can be found in Switzerland (7) [a]

15 Mussolini in a state, engulfed by emotional pressure from **femme fatale** (10) [q,cii,e]

19 Sinned in a colourful way, according to some (6) [b]

20 **Charge** account application (6) [o,d]

23 This philosopher must be turning in his grave! (4) [b]

24 **Prolific** output of a **no-name poet** soon to be discovered (4) [h,u]

6

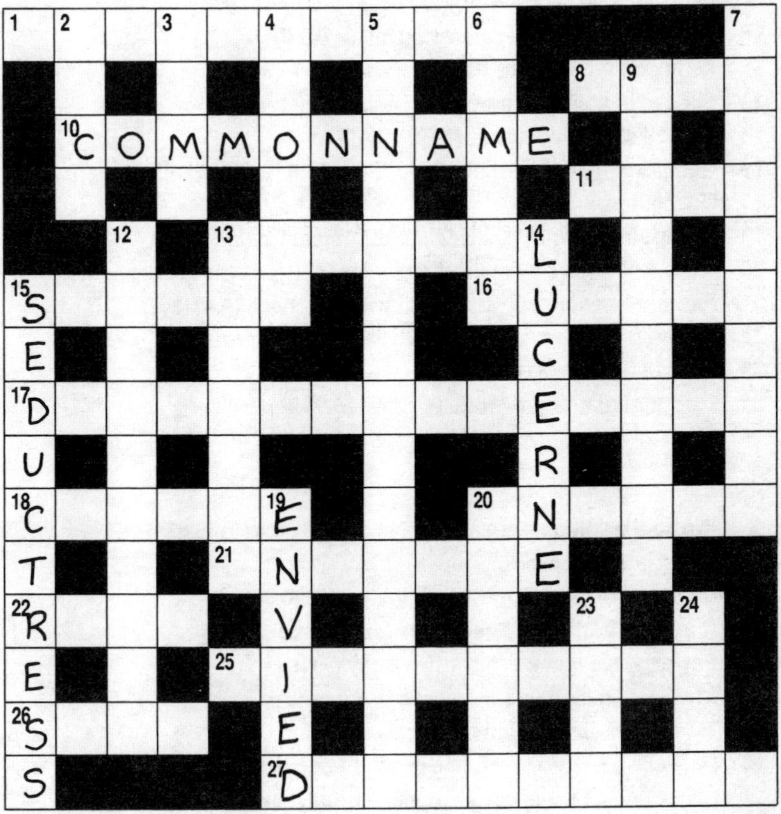
COMMONNAME
LUCERNE
SEDUCTRESS
ENVIED

Across

1   Fool one met in company with **Shakespeare's Lieutenant** (6) [o,e,o,q]
5   **Stirred** by tower in part of India (8) [e]
9   All clues read over so that I can begin **puzzle** (8) [ni]
10 **Unpleasent smell** from roast enchilada (6) [h]
11 Farm plot ploughed up to make **raised area** (8) [ci]
12 In church, journalist **moved imperceptibly** (6) [d,o]
13 Typical state of America? (8) [b]
15 Composer from the Arctic Circle? (4) [b]
17 Get out **basin** (4) [a]
19 **Counselling** avoids tangled lines of communication (8) [ci,d,o]
20 **Achieve balance** by redirecting squats (6) [l]
21 **Firmness** proverbially associated with soft touch (4,4) [b,q]
22 **Colourful expressions** describe island in hell of mess (6) [o,e,cii]
23 **She** is a beauty! (8) [d]
24 Late pilot of **a Tiger Moth, perhaps** (5,3) [d,piii]
25 **Mistakes** are almost frightening! (6) [j]

Down

2   **Praise** a revolting peasant surrounding the pass (8) [e,q]
3   **Generous** with wine in shop (8) [e]
4   Duck routed as lark **flew much higher** (9) [o,ci]
5   A mismatch claimed as **grounds for divorce** (15) [a]
6   **Power** of ten found in blemished copy (7) [e,ci]
7   **Mexican stockman** ran and caught Superman (8) [o,d]
8   **Two-faced** die-hard left in disarray (8) [cii,o]
14 Cool cheat needed to manage this **kind of bar**? (9) [ci]
15 Check one who sounds like **unconventional artist** (8) [i,b]
16 Call up falling inspiration in **beginning again** (8) [e,g]
17 **Unwilling recruit thus led** to be hearty convert (2,3,3) [ci]
18 Argumentative **student**? (8) [b]
19 A non-drinker comes to pre-empt **the endeavour** (7) [o,d]

7

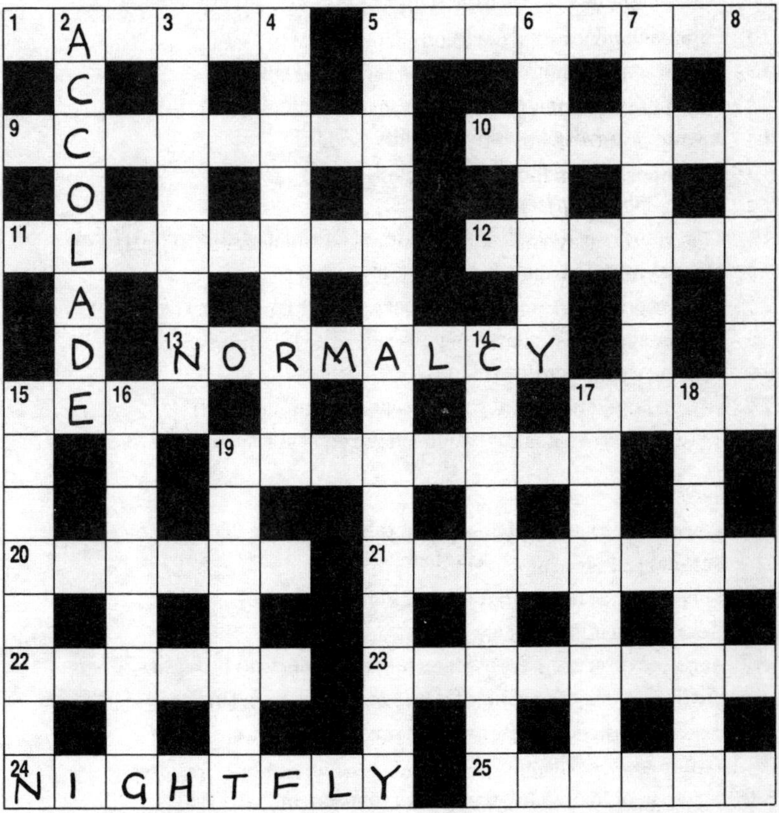
ACCOLADE
NORMALCY
NIGHTFLY

Across

1   **Funny** mineral found in mountain (7) [e]
5   **Desert, we hear,** is yellow (7) [i]
9   Central aim of a lord's ball? (6,5) [b,piii]
10   Imperial heavyweight (3) [b,pii]
11   **Aged chap** sometimes referred to father (3,3) [a]
13   **Highlights importance** of bearings outside lock (8) [e,o]
15   **Ambassador** of outstanding quality (10) [a]
16   **Lots** may contain number initally (4) [e,nii]
18   Fly-by-night? (4) [b,pi]
19   Translator in the saddling enclosure is for **the high jump** (10) [o,e]
22   **Churchman** lancing a boil! (8) [ci]
23   **One who is promised** public money gets nearly all of it (6) [f]
25   **Saucer** could be under frying oil initially (3) [ni]
26   Forecasts **possibilities** (11) [a]
28   Ensured operation **legal with this agreement** (3,4) [ci]
29   Really unknown quantity included in **reference system** (7) [o,e]

Down

1   Mozart, for example, has no right **to write music** (7) [j]
2   **Soft earth** in Bermuda (3) [h]
3   Copper can hold record for **being guilty** (8) [o,e,o]
4   **Hear** old pianist (4) [i,s,u]
5   Accurate directions for cooking **lobster or shrimp** (10) [cii,o]
6   Rustles up, perhaps, a bit of **a late evening snack** (6) [h]
7   **Bearing witness** at trial after topping relation (11) [d,j]
8   **Tudor** soap, perhaps! (7) [a]
12   Where people used to go under for punishment? (7,4) [b]
14   Engineers coach **someone who holds back** (10) [o,d]
17   **Hooked** dace and half tiddlers swam furiously (8) [cii,j]
18   It's a **cheek** writing such an article (7) [a]
20   Relieved after short Greek is **bribed** (7) [o,d]
21   **Cockney eyes** butcher's wares (6) [a]
24   Each one is **a fairy** (4) [d,o]
27   **King's** dog called this? (3) [a]

8

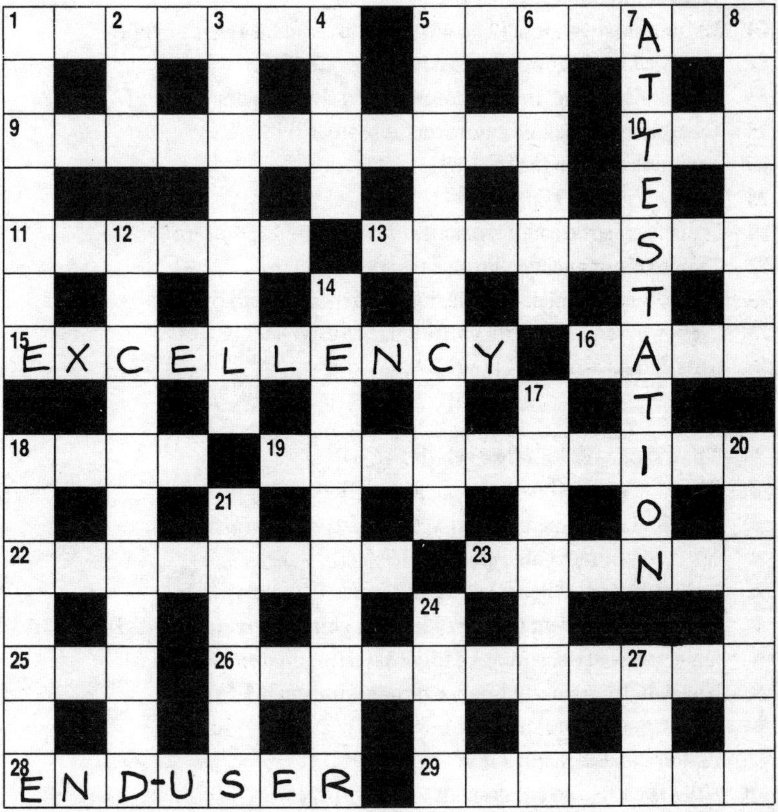
EXCELLENCY
END-USER
ATTESTATION

Across

1   **Settles** advance payment with teams (8) [d]

5   Part of Paul's foot (6) [b]

10 **Honest** direction (15) [a]

11 **Extortionist** squeezed one who used to tread the boards (7) [a]

12 Troubled by danger with Eastern **magnate** (7) [cii,o]

13 Back in Baghdad, no canard surrounds **this crawler** (8) [h,g]

15 **Complete** setback without army reserves (5) [u,g,o,e]

17 **Business** custom (5) [a]

19 Spilt acid near **bright light** (8) [ci]

22 Property displayed by those who 7 (7) [b,r]

23 **Witty remark** made during Tripos term (7) [h]

24 Mechanical study of current interest, no doubt (15) [b]

25 Somewhere to sit before you prepare to drive off? (6) [b]

26 **Small, fleet** vessels (8) [a,pi]

Down

1   None spoke of this **close relative** (6) [i]

2   Where to get the lowdown on cheap offers? (7,8) [b]

3   **Silly** fool in charge (7) [d,o]

4   There is turbulent **air up above** (5) [ci]

6   **Fully briefed,** sailor takes a rest outside (7) [o,d,e]

7   Endure punishment to the point when **you appear dead** (5,5,5) [d]

8   Duly send letters, sorted **hastily** (8) [ci]

9   **Not watching** unusual stance of one who's in? (3,5) [a]

14 **Teller** ran back to desert with gold (8) [g,d]

16 **Players** that managers don't get on with! (8) [a]

18 **Give the right** to call a spade *A Spade* (6) [a]

20 The end of the road for Cleopatra? (7) [b]

21 I ran from here when the Shah reigned (6) [pii,b]

23 Two boys **belonging to Her Majesty**? (5) [d]

9

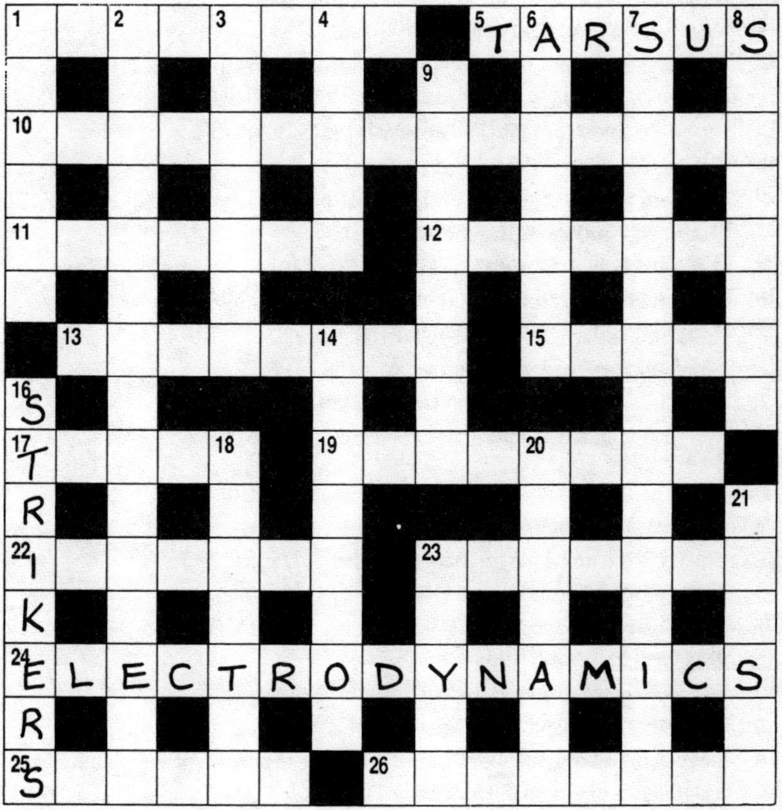
TARSUS
STRIKERS
ELECTRODYNAMICS

Across

1 Wrench open the top of **drain** (6) [l]

4 A trapper might **draw on this** (3,5) [ci]

10 Mother put her Malcolm in **a type of underwear** (7) [h]

11 Girl has spoken **of local chief** (7) [d]

12 Listens again to one no good initially after **further practice** (10) [d,o,ni]

13 Sort out sink **for use on 4?** (4) [ci,r]

15 Suspend boxer for **looking cowed** (7) [d]

17 Picture set for this **field event** (4-3) [d]

19 Problem originating at the back **part of horse's leg** (7) [nii,d]

21 Roam with pie about **the shops** (7) [ci]

23 **Hit** a seedy kind of joint (4) [a]

24 **Dignified** queues form at Street reunion (10) [cii,o]

27 **Tiny** little fellow from the start of 10 (7) [d,r]

28 Knot attaches **men's fashion accessories** (7) [d]

29 Any chits rewritten for this **old countryman?** (8) [ci,pii]

30 Reptiles with a calculating nature, presumably (6) [b]

Down

1 Teachers' joint **post** (9) [d]

2 **Butler's paradise** paradoxically nowhere (7) [q,ci]

3 **Seize** animals on public land, we hear (10) [d,i]

5 **Recollect** nice mires (9) [v,ci]

6 **Rewards** for a spy, perhaps (4) [ci]

7 Score then cut **this vegetable** (7) [d]

8 **Registers** expensive car (5) [a]

9 Low to the south-east, you'll see the European species of these animals (4) [d,o]

14 Take in **embrace** (10) [a]

16 Information details Italians' **most sensitive areas!** (9) [d,j]

18 **Passes over** stanza in Arts form (9) [e,ci]

20 Spruce, poplar, ironwood, nutmeg, nicotinia, elder, yew: all originate **here** (7) [ni]

22 Religious Education old choir **need** (7) [o,s,d]

23 **Searches** for companies containing medical graduate (5) [o,e]

25 Artists' sugar-daddy? (4) [b]

26 Were Shem, Ham and Japheth partly raised by **this wet-nurse?** (4) [h,g]

10

A Short History of the Crossword

The tradition of acrostics and word-play stretches right back to Greek and Roman times: Cicero, for instance, records how the sibyls used riddles to prophesy the future, and there are various well-documented examples of how early Christians employed enigmatic devices to reveal their message to other believers.

Yet it was not until the Victorian age that word games started to gain ground as a form of popular entertainment, with the appearance of numerous books of puzzles and brain-teasers. Inventive though they were, however, the Victorians never really progressed beyond a simple form of puzzle based on the word square, a group of words arranged to read the same both horizontally and vertically.

In fact, it was the Americans who took things a stage further. On December 21, 1913, the first genuine crossword to be published in a newspaper appeared among a number of more conventional puzzles in the Sunday *Fun* supplement of the *New York World*. Called a 'Word Cross', it consisted of a diamond-shaped grid with definitional clues to the intersecting solutions and was compiled by Arthur Wynne, an immigrant from Liverpool. This type of puzzle proved so popular that by 1923 most American newspapers had a crossword; by this time, the craze had started to spread to Britain, where it quickly became accepted as a national pastime.

The first regular crossword in the UK was published by the *Sunday Express* in 1924, while puzzles started appearing in the *Daily Telegraph* a year later. The *Times* lays claim to being the first British paper to have a crossword appearing on a daily basis (February 1, 1930) – although there is some dispute about this.

These early crosswords had essentially straightforward definitional clues with barely a hint of cryptic in them. Indeed, American puzzles have remained definitional to this day – even though some of the clues and solutions are highly obscure. British crosswords, on the other hand, gradually started to move away from the established, literal type of clue in the direction of devices such as anagrams (simply labelled 'anagram' at first), double definitions, obscure indications and all the other misleading strategies that are now a commonplace part of the cryptic crossword as we know it today.

The conventions that govern the shape of the diagram, and the rules of fair play in setting clues developed largely through a process of evolution – much like the English constitution. Attempts have been made by famous setters such as Afrit and Ximenes to frame rules for writing crossword clues: much currently received wisdom is based on their work. For those who are interested in studying the subject of clueing, Don Manley's *Crossword Manual* (Chambers) provides an entertaining and accessible introduction.

Crosswords 11 - 20

This section starts off with puzzles of about the same standard as the first ten, gradually increasing in difficulty. The more difficult puzzles towards the end are of a standard roughly on a par with an easy to average puzzle in one of the broadsheet dailies. Once again, neither the clues nor the solutions contain any words that should require the use of a dictionary.

In these crosswords, however, we have not highlighted the definitional element of the clues: you will have to go through the puzzles and sort this out for yourself. Neither are there any partially completed grids.

What you do still get are the indications of clue devices bracketed after each clue. (You should by now be fairly familiar with the alphabetical labelling used for the more common devices.) This and the **Two-way Crossword Glossary** should enable you to tackle most of the clues in these puzzles without too much difficulty. Once again, if you do have problems with a particular clue, consult the **Help** section.

Across

1   Full of beans after drinking this? (6) [b]

4 & 2 *Dn* Ship's Officer goes to Welsh town to find chatty bird (7,5) [d,q]

9   Head's golden rule, we're told (9) [i]

10   Pole becomes end of handle (5) [nii,d]

11   Bury together (5) [a]

12   'And smooth as monumental —' (Othello) (9) [q]

13   Atone for resistance from former corsair (7) [o,d,f]

15   Dress one might be right appearing in (6) [ci,d,o,e]

17   Purpose in putting energy into explosive (6) [d,o,e]

19   Beg to replant a National Trust tree (7) [cii,o]

22   Furnish books catering for future needs (9) [d,o]

24   Resistance unit stumbled through ack-ack on this beach (5) [cii,o]

26   Sound from soprano is exquisite (5) [h]

27   Take choir about Jerusalem, for example (9) [ci]

28   Grid used outside for training climbers (7) [b]

29   Lost hot tip in here? (6) [e,nii]

Down

1   Whim of island church (7) [d,o]

2   See 4 *Ac* (5)

3   Old chief officer with irate outburst will tear you off a strip (9) [o,d,ci]

4   Late Passover get-together (7) [d,pi,pii]

5   Dad's gratitude, of course (5) [d]

6   Girl, with exercise, fit for anything! (9) [d,o,u]

7   He wrote not a line (6) [d,o]

8   Work I took in to get narcotic (6) [o,d]

14   Peter to act silently in this Christmas show? (9) [q,d]

16   Withdraws nothing inside that has influence on past events (9) [e,o]

18   Created space to protect one's pedal extremities (7) [ci,u]

19   Object denoted entirety (6) [f]

20   Attempt to chase inside for ornamentation (7) [e]

21   Pest in reconstructed instrument (6) [ci]

23   Immaculate conception? (5) [a]

25   Othello reported as Latin lover (5) [i]

11

Across

1   You need these, we hear, to see small particles (6) [i]
5   Take cab back to car at end of casino game (8) [j,d]
9   Girl Scout leader occasionally seen after dark (5,3) [a]
10 Piece of metal is sometimes very flexible (6) [h]
11 Preoccupied with eye, by the sound of it (8) [b,i]
12 Guide's often instructed thus to corrupt (4,2) [a]
13 Frenchman in grenade explosion finds policeman (8) [o,cii]
15 Goddess leads a double life apparently (4) [d]
17 Addition of lavish detail (4) [j]
19 Travelling salesman gets pain right after visiting minister (8) [cii,d]
20 Emphatic opening gambit to use (6) [nii,d]
21 13, for example, creates a pure one (8) [r,ci]
22 Many going to Ravel symphony given cause for amazement (6) [o,cii]
23 Most can't vote before reaching this age (8) [a]
24 True saint out East can be barely discerned (8) [cii,j,o]
25 Lying low to avoid this punishment, perhaps (6) [a]

Down

2   Models rearrange a rap song (8) [ci]
3   Enclosures for animals eating heather (8) [pi,e]
4   Powdered steer horn used to make pastry (9) [ci]
5   Protection for despatch rider on Russian front? (9,6) [b]
6   Boxer, perhaps, since he reformed (7) [q,ci]
7   Store's closing: I take two of what's left (8) [pi,nii,d]
8   Hardy heroine about to end prayer for meek nature (8) [q,e]
14 Graduate going to express suspicion to Indian landlord finds his boss (9) [o,d]
15 5 *Dn* also worn at this engagement (8) [r]
16 Fashionable drink lacking body one recalled (2,6) [d]
17 Ready to edit red paper (8) [ci]
18 Ten fauns gambolling free (8) [ci]
19 One in a jetty is among the first (7) [e]

12

Across

1 Single log (6) [a]
4 Travel document issued after dinner invitation (8) [a,pii]
10 Royal mistress with an early form of beehive! (9) [b,q]
11 Hold back inside about fantasy (5) [e,o]
12 Kid soldier, perhaps, to run away (8) [d]
13 Instruction to loquacious luggage handler? (4,2) [b]
15 The aching part everyone separately considered (4) [h]
17 Put in grave appearance for formal meeting (9) [d]
20 Asia, for example, is temperate (9) [a]
21 What seer discerned partly from entrails (4) [h]
24 Conveyed after a second compliance (6) [o,d]
25 Condense company papers containing Maxwell's initial (8) [o,e,nii]
28 Area round the centre of Genoa is part of ancient amphitheatre (5) [e,nii]
29 Copied from chopped-up cedar tree (9) [ci]
30 The cure for love-sickness, perhaps (8) [b]
31 A churchman started to become confused (6) [d,o,d]

Down

1 Substituted parcel Ed repackaged (8) [ci]
2 Reach tiptop heavenly body (5) [d,nii]
3 Actually about League member (6) [o,d]
5 Light-hearted tune has funny ending (4) [d,ni]
6 Stupidly deviates from bedtime prescription (8) [ci]
7 Finished wearing original headgear after flood (9) [d,nii,d]
8 Plant used to split atom (6) [d,ci]
9 Part of the hole, we understand (9) [b,i]
14 Strengthen control for the Church (9) [d,o]
16 High-flier's point of view (5,4) [b]
18 Upright Pole used to fly the flag (8) [piii,a]
19 Uneven description of defective 1 *Ac*, perhaps (3,5) [a,r]
22 Best start pineapple without second fruit (6) [nii,d,j]
23 Sort of paste to be avoided in middle age, if possible (6) [a]
26 Praise for former charge, we hear (5) [d,i]
27 Support model with tiresome child (4) [d,o]

13

Across

1   Who knows? This type of question remains unanswered (10) [b]
8   Block the return of large sums of money (4) [g]
10 Tacky American game? (5,5) [b]
11 Somewhere to store a variety of paints (4) [cii]
13 Cast light on information about file (7) [e]
15 Going upstairs (6) [a,pii]
16 Musical movements started by Rossini, Offenbach, Nielsen, Debussy, Orff and Schoenberg (6) [ni]
17 Crazy interpretation of a dream has a kind of charm (3,2,1,5,4) [ci,ci]
18 Open display (6) [a]
20 Awkward refusal to race in Kentucky (6) [d,o,e,o]
21 Paying organization to keep quiet in Barking (7) [cii,o,piii]
22 Standard article from Roman constitution (4) [cii,j]
25 Could be right in not describing persistent offender (10) [a,j]
26 Indian in a trance might say a mantra backwards (4) [h,g]
27 Of the sinner reformed, the saint is this! (10) [ci,u]

Down

2   Barely tolerate mediocre journalist (4) [a]
3   Right advice about holiday (4) [o,e]
4   What could come about from the disintegration of Ulster (6) [ci]
5   Vision of the present day (9,6) [b]
6   Minor points separating two sides (6) [o,e,o]
7   Shot purely in order to produce chair covering (10) [ci]
9   Liberals once described a policy for the motorist (5,5) [a]
12 Hungry flier fed by prior arrangement (4,2,4) [ci]
13 Faint appearance of 5 in Dickens story? (7) [a,q,r]
14 Lack of significance Macbeth accorded to biography (7) [a,q]
15 Well-known figure at Lloyds? (6,4) [b]
19 Plane that flew both north and south here in the States (6) [a,piii]
20 Thing assembled to support King's champion (6) [cii,o,u]
23 Authorized Napoleon's island retreat (4) [g]
24 Half man, half beast, this creature is still single! (4) [d,o]

14

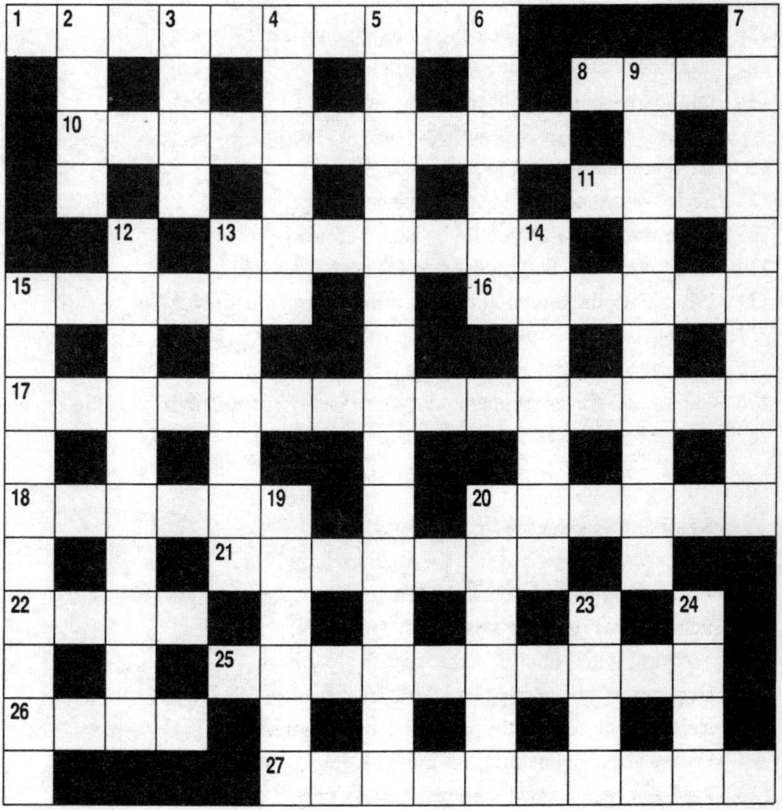

Across

1   Acting royally? (10) [b,q]
6   Large chunk of material from physics laboratory (4) [h]
10 Seafood starters often can taste of pretty unpalatable stuff (7) [ni]
11 Clergyman who searched every crook and nanny! (7) [b,q]
12 Craft for river trips out East (9) [d,cii,o]
13 Barnaby taking girl's head in rough embrace (5) [q,nii,e]
14 *La Mer* transposed for another country (5) [ci]
15 Filled up uncomfortably as it is fed (9) [ci]
17 Lorded over and loved to embrace bird (9) [e]
20 This animal, by right, could be a stinker! (5) [j]
21 Get by, we hear, playing bit part (5) [i,a]
23 Gall and urethra opening may be affected by such a fever (9) [cii,nii]
25 Nasty stain the result of Indian upset, perhaps (3,4) [b]
26 Beat chap for touching line (7) [d]
27 Ringing this before dinner could make George cross, perhaps (4) [a,piii]
28 Champion's exploit in a French action (10) [d,e]

Down

1   Examine soft dress (5) [o,d]
2   Sadly contemplates net loss for medium term (9) [cii,j]
3   Former fairy psychically linked through trial and error (14) [d]
4   Sack infernal American waitress 7) [d]
5   Emerging when finally on the way up (7) [nii,d]
7   Idle partner gets worried look? (5) [cii,o,u]
8   Exchange goods in the end to get drinks from him (9) [e]
9   Writing prose concerned editorial (14) [ci]
14 Changing colour – what a ruddy cheek (9) [b]
16 'Our meddling — Misshapes the beauteous forms of things'
    (Wordsworth) (9) [q]
18 Screw up directions after getting drunk? (7) [d,o]
19 Conscript loses raft in river (7) [e]
22 Knot tied in end of tie for remembrance (5) [cii,e,nii]
24 Trade uncommonly highly thought of (5) [ci]

15

Across

1   Younger son preparing for commission (5) [a]

4   Grew less from ploughed acres? Indeed! (9) [ci,e]

9   Poetic description of Snow White, perhaps (3,6) [b,piii]

10 Ron taking exercise? On the contrary, flat out (5) [e,o]

11 Join in token listening (6) [h]

12 Treaders worked with pointed teeth (8) [ci]

14, 16, 22 *Dn*, 29 *Ac*, 6 *Dn* Classic war story told about early Italian state (7,3,4,2,3,5,6) [q,i,d]

16 See 14 (4)

19 Odes rewritten to a certain measure (4) [ci]

20 Wobble unsteadily about and note regular movement (3,3,4) [cii,e,o]

22 Oddly covers debts, having lost five hundred in ignominious fashion (8) [f,o,e]

23 Discover cause of noise (6) [a]

26 Characteristic of one in small Italian restaurant (5) [o,e]

27 Device levels stone (9) [d]

28 Concerned about revision in tax demand initially (9) [o,cii,nii]

29 See 14 (5)

Down

1   With Italian nurse Edward struggled (9) [d,o]

2   Do well to lose trainee from post (5) [j]

3   Impale and paralyse (8) [a]

4   It's senseless to cull four hundred more (4) [l]

5   By the sound of it, would add a further hundred years to this anniversary (10) [i,b]

6   See 14 (6)

7   Brief dip leaves something to be desired (9) [d]

8   Fear of the cadre a democracy entertains (5) [h]

13 Early botanists used their slabs for dissection (10) [ci]

15 Criticize actors after one entrance (9) [d,o,d]

17 Teutonic sound coming from manger before reconstruction (3,6) [d,cii]

18 Control often necessary in settlement of insurance claims (8) [a]

21 Brown in charge of the country (6) [d,o]

22 See 14 (3,2)

24 God, how stuck up! (2,3) [a]

25 Raised for food, we're told (4) [i]

Across

1   Hired hand at the wheel? (9) [b]
6   The old way, right, is more discreet (5) [s,d,o]
9   *High Noon* hailed by the Irish? (3,2,3,7) [piii,b]
10 She also returns in comfort (6) [e,g]
11 Take off belt and repair accident damage (8) [a]
13 Tradesmen who may use auto-suggestion (3,7) [b]
14 Battled, we're told, for this stronghold (4) [i]
16 Poor sweetheart embraced by chap (4) [nii,e]
17 Removed thread from such tinted weaving (10) [ci]
19 Conservative Bar hesitate to find 6 *Ac* (8) [o,d,r]
20 Memorized material that is not fresh but peculiarly apt (3,3) [d,ci]
23 Young genius, highly valued in company issue (10,5) [e,o,d]
24 Try to experience flavour (5) [a]
25 A Green right to reject this power source (9) [cii,o]

Down

1   Quotes sound views (5) [i]
2   Suitability of relevant points (15) [d,o]
3   Struggle with the stiff part of the match (5,3) [ci]
4   Leader of Halle in English Chamber Orchestra making noisy comeback (4) [ni,o,e]
5   Enumerate initial requirements revised for pay (10) [cii,nii]
6   What airline pilots do to arouse feelings? (4,2) [a]
7   Extremely painful compass direction for rambler, perhaps! (5,2,3,5) [b]
8   Remembered with sense of loss your last bird, Edward (9) [nii,d,o]
12 Top botanist down in the heather floundering about (10) [nii,d,e]
13 Light relief for the funny bone? (5,4) [a]
15 What 1 *Ac* may do for officer's vehicle (5,3) [r,a]
18 Take out this form (6) [a]
21 Half-timbered royal house? (5) [b]
22 Scottish poet detailed stream in his vernacular (4) [j]

17

Across

1   Discussion commonly held among members (6) [b,piii]
4   Crude SAS manoeuvre involving second-hand vehicles (4,4) [ci,b]
10 Wooster's farewell to broken old pipe (6,3) [d,ci]
11 Though silent, a citizen's contribution is understood (5) [h]
12 Hesitation after Gustav starts to produce a gun from here (7) [d,q]
13 Uneasy when it veers about (7) [ci]
14 March past when this begins (5) [b]
15 Hardy people take hits back and forth (8) [g,d]
18 Thunderous sea unusual central element in his paintings (8) [h]
20 Shock a quiet friend (5) [o,d]
23 Rig vote to produce a loss of balance (7) [ci]
25 Books suitable for bed? (7) [a]
26 Strange means to identify people (5) [ci]
27 Expansive conversation with non-native (9) [d,pii,j]
28 Representative figures found in American house (8) [b,piii]
29 Popular sayings of present times (6) [o,d]

Down

1   European aeronaut noted by Wagner (8) [a,q]
2   Young chicken is trapped right inside the boiler (7) [o,e]
3   Sneaks revealed Archer's inside story (4,5) [q,piii,e]
5   Outstanding, of course, in a strange way (14) [d]
6   Fruit consumed in the outskirts of Damascus (5) [e,ni]
7   Man from 1 *Dn* guarantees price-cutting here (7) [r,j,b]
8   Tester may be the one who compiles this (6) [ci]
9   For this commentator, in particular, cricket's about having a drink afterwards! (6,8) [d]
16 Prepare group for the militia (9) [d]
17 'Nor all, that —, gold' (Gray) (8) [q]
19 Eight going to Crewe, we're told – but not by train! (7) [b,i]
21 What you might be doing when suffering right inside (7) [e,o]
22 First lady's not disheartened entering functions (6) [d,j]
24 Patch where badger may be found (5) [a,d]

18

Across

1   Main cause of internal disorder (11) [b]
9   Barrie's darling dog (4) [piii,q]
10 Abbreviated solution that an 'S' could stand for? (5,6) [b,pi,pii,piii]
11 You could listen to this passage of Bach if I turned it on (2,2) [h]
14 Potentially successful idea for a first course (7) [a]
16 React explosively to partner after card game (6) [cii,o]
17 Red soldier in custody (6) [e]
18 An extra vestment for the priest (3) [d,o]
20 Mysteriously recasts Garbo, perhaps (7) [ci]
21 Frenzied love bites may ultimately lead to a weight problem! (7) [o,cii,nii]
22 One who was entitled to come in from the cold (3) [q]
24 Men are manipulated to change designation (6) [ci]
26 Georgia tea served with fashionable cake (6) [o,d,o]
27 Malicious gossip about conservative footwear (7) [o,e]
28 Dissolute firm (4) [a]
31 Circus act performing nude, we are told (7,4) [d,i]
32 Lion family misses start of journey (4) [j]
33 Widespread feeling after Mafeking, no doubt! (5,6) [b]

Down

2   Reflective nymph? (4) [b]
3   Type of gold found in the street (4) [e,o]
4   Virgin is hounded, by sound of it (6) [i]
5   Opening below the bridge (7) [b]
6   Sounds like bird could be done to a turn on this (6) [i]
7   Excellent scheme for making money perhaps (7,4) [b]
8   Sat in sun abroad with a bored expression (3,2,3,3) [t,d,piii]
12 Former panel reassembled to produce changes in sentencing policy (5,6) [ci]
13 Striking team at the Oval, for instance (7,4) [b]
14 Mists around river condensed to form smaller tributaries (7) [e,o]
15 Restoration novel has genuine binding (7) [e]
18 Animal stuck in crevasse (3) [h]
19 Issue booty unevenly (3) [nii]
23 Chewing a pea can be a cure for all ills (7) [ci]
25 Claire, head over heels, is sweet (6) [k]
26 Arrange to remove article from ramshackle store (6) [j,ci]
29 Victim Mabel beheaded (4) [j]
30 Open bar with key (4) [d,o]

19

Across

1   Individual student accepted though not very bright (5) [e,o]
4   Charmed by oriental woman who is fascinating in bed (9) [o,d,e]
9   Victory at this battle (9) [b]
10 Dog with no tail given an outing (5) [j]
11 Not in suitable uniform (6) [d]
12 Leave vehicle on road near Mayfair (4-4) [d]
14 Writers of playful material? (10) [b]
16 Retreat before this erupts! (4) [g]
19 Harps on about snag (4) [ci]
20 Fluid runs from this plant (10) [d]
22 Sole power game (8) [a]
23 A paper edited to do this daily (6) [ci]
26 Greene Man entitled to a bronze medal? (5) [piii,q,a]
27 Might publish this as principal concern (4,5) [d]
28 Perfume from scrap of cloth in France (9) [e]
29 Shot in the dark part of rogue's strategy (5) [h]

Down

1   New copper turned on Organization (9) [o,cii,piii]
2   Inclined to speak fast (5) [i]
3   Prehistoric description of Shakespearian lovers (8) [b,q]
4   Insects frequently annoying the programmer (4) [a]
5   Licence that is backed by partner's guarantees (10) [d,o]
6   Lines mades by carts meandering round the middle of Carrickfergus (6) [ci,nii,e]
7   'She should have died —' (Macbeth) (9) [q]
8   Odd, for example, to resort to subterfuge (5) [cii,o]
13 Remain strangely calm, perhaps, within the presence of this remarkable fellow (7,3) [ci]
15 Plate banked mainly here in South America (9) [b]
17 Following shock, these make for a smooth ride (9) [u]
18 Exchanging partner somewhere in the East End (8) [d]
21 Spinner used to play snooker occasionally (6) [a]
22 Distinctive idea if combined with French word (5) [d]
24 Directions to girl to follow (5) [o,d]
25 German wine sounds like it comes from this (4) [u,i]

20

Famous and Infamous Clues

In the previous feature on the history of the crossword, we mentioned the way in which the art of the crossword has gradually evolved over the years. Every so often, a clue will appear which is so original or so elegant that it genuinely stretches the imagination and is treasured by many solvers. Such clues are often discussed in the correspondence columns of daily newspapers or in the more rarefied pages of the magazine *Crossword*.

Perhaps one of the most famous is: **1)** A jammed cylinder (5,4). This is a delightfully concise single-definition cryptic clue, which depends principally on a rather sticky pun on the word 'jammed'. Another, using a very similar trick is: **2)** A wicked thing (6).

There are various unwritten rules about what can and can't be appear in crosswords – although to some extent, this is up to the discretion of the editor. By and large, anything 'distressing' or 'vulgar' (as marked in the dictionary) is usually avoided in both clues and solutions. Two of the more risqué clues to have appeared in daily newspaper puzzles were **3)** What you might find at gay weddings in the isles (8) and **4)** Like occupants getting down to business (9). Brand names and many of the more transient phenomena of the popular media are also deliberately avoided in most mainstream puzzles.

Of course, certain indications and devices crop up very commonly. Often seen is a variation on **5)** Back door (4) – probably originally published in the *Telegraph* and featured *idem in alio* in one of our own puzzles. Sometimes, compilers get very upset to see their clues reused in other puzzles, although given the ultimate limitations on how certain solutions can be constructed and the way that things tend to stick in the subconscious only to reappear as apparently original ideas, it's scarcely surprising that this should happen occasionally. One clue that caused the sparks to fly was the excellent **6)** Judge taking tea-break after *Times* puzzle (8), which appeared in both the *Times* and the *FT* from different compilers.

The clues most favoured by regular solvers, however, are those which require a real leap of the imagination on either very flimsy or very misleading evidence. Try these on for size:

    7) HIJKLMNO (5) **8)** O (8,6) **9)** I say nothing (3)
        10) A stiff examination (4,6)

Answers to all these below!

10) POST MORTEM
8) CIRCULAR LETTER **9)** EGO [say = EG + nothing = O]
4) SQUATTING **5)** ROOD **6)** ESTIMATE **7)** WATER [H to O]
1) SWISS ROLL **2)** CANDLE **3)** HEBRIDES [HE|BRIDES]

Crosswords 21 - 30

Now you are on your own. Crosswords 21 - 30 contain no on-grid assistance or indications of clue devices. (Of course, all the clues are explained in detail, as usual, in the **Help** section.)

These puzzles go from average difficulty to a standard that is probably equivalent to a prize puzzle in a weekend edition of one of the 'big' dailies. A few of the clues are quite difficult and one or two of the solutions may require the help of dictionary to check – unless you want to look them up at the back of this book, of course!

Remember that even in a difficult crossword not *all* the clues are difficult. Look through each clue before you start, as advised in **Practical Hints on Solving**: you will certainly be able to get quite a few of them – which will help you tackle the tough ones.

Once you have come to terms with these crosswords, you will have encountered nearly all of the common devices used by setters. You will be in a position to have a go at any of the daily paper puzzles with a fair degree of confidence. From now on, it's mainly a question of building up speed and really starting to enjoy the dazzling array of verbal deception that is displayed every day of the week on the inside or back page of your favourite newspaper.

Across

1 Mr Fox's invitation to return to reality? (4,4,2,5)
9 Might oral constitution result in this kind of power? (9)
10 No taxi back for painter (5)
11 The last word in formal correspondence (6)
12 Help to measure extremes of company trend (8)
14 Small particle I found in canal could be part of body (10)
16 Forbid animal doctor to have duck (4)
18 Gloomy dean partly endorsing evangelism (4)
19 Garibaldi might be found in here! (7,3)
21 King overthrown August 5 in Sweden (8)
22 Go if an unfit Argentine driver appears (6)
25 Working: not out with us, note! (2,3)
26 Source of illumination on board? (5,4)
27 Dispose of lions quickly? (2,1,7,5)

Down

1 Working out object of a devious brain (11,4)
2 Small contribution sounded theoretically possible (5)
3 Flash room back in prison (8)
4 Keep them about you for amusement? (4)
5 Moderate a northern church society, perhaps (10)
6 Plants firmly into foundations after measurement (6)
7 Put back in touch after Bill was ignored (9)
8 Holiday pair just hitched (9,6)
13 Fires built to create an obstruction in legislative assembly (10)
15 Bitter bark sometimes prescribed in small measure (9)
17 Hair may glow in light (8)
20 Manage to perform twice in a different way (4,2)
23 Country store by the sound of it (5)
24 No 16 for Scottish port (4)

21

Across

1   Dismiss priests for wearing this? (9)
6   Beat's changed back to old beat (5)
9   Some latent heat retained in the crucible, for example (7)
10   Anchorage found by Othello getting home at midnight (7)
11   Refine inert chemical (5)
12   Countermeasure contains nothing which responds to pressure (9)
14   Hill fort loses leader in revolt (3)
15   Bolstering up invalid as cure's near (11)
17   Eye queue reported to be greater than usual! (11)
19   Fool around on the dance floor (3)
20   Could be a help when changing in the gloom out East (9)
22   One kind of wood is perfect (5)
24   Clearly making a profit (7)
26   Troops not intent on evening stopover (7)
27   Surely losing equanimity initially could make one like this (5)
28   Top of weapon used for frontal attack? (9)

Down

1   Fabric, for example, removed from seating (5)
2   He adjusted reactor (7)
3   Aspire to this in the City (9)
4   Big-headed about position (11)
5   Bad actor allowed to leave *Hamlet* (3)
6   Sweeper found in the garden (5)
7   Hit with small glove (7)
8   Enthusiasm displayed by keen Head (9)
13   Stalwart upset creeps on board (11)
14   Parts clipped off decorations (9)
16   Terrier and vet almost upset another dog (9)
18   Animal on this would stagger around run (7)
19   Power to begin again and take for granted (7)
21   Congregation gathered from Italy (5)
23   First, five ludicrous characters can be easily seen (5)
25   Gains lost in empty talk (3)

22

Across

1   Meet a payment, so to speak (6)
4   Nowadays, junta organized by second staff officer (8)
10 French poet of the pastoral tradition? (9)
11 Failure to finish trial before recess (5)
12 Artist to draw explorer (7)
13 Sells noted stories, we're told (7)
14 New look at the top is a washout (5)
15 Fundamentals worry steelmen (8)
18 Casual garment might suit those starting to play golf? (3,5)
20 Philosopher introduced plebeian leaders as top orators (5)
23 Subject in the National Curriculum, no doubt!
25 Proposition made by me to her (7)
26 Colourful addition to foundation (5)
27 Pointed proposal gets gangster overwrought (9)
28 I object on board to friend sharing my cabin (8)
29 Engineers defy extremes to put things right (6)

Down

1   Do they listen to your accounts? (8)
2   CIA leaves strict order for a tank (7)
3   These may be raised by sailors celebrating on board such vessels (9)
5   Direction taken by Orpheus – and the reason he got lost! (14)
6   In the dark until reforms (5)
7   Employ a soft tip (7)
8   Article first adhered to by believer (6)
9   Irishmen vote Prime Minister in to deal with growing scarcity of resources (14)
16 Dam said, for example, to be a stopgap measure (9)
17 Officially inform all youngsters (8)
19 Where you might find food for soldiers at breakfast time (7)
21 Called in time, upset, to settle (7)
22 Make a killing by backing this horse (3,3)
24 Muesli nearly all regurgitated by this part of the intestine (5)

23

Across

1   Bully's order to slackers in the cotton field, perhaps! (4,2)
4   Lover of 13 found plant on mountain (8)
10 Chairs get upset in German house (9)
11 D.G. Rossetti described as being involved in various Movements (5)
12 To which Browning's rider sprang (7)
13 Unruly lout is king's youngest son (7)
14 Naive way to treat birthmarks (5)
15 Newly named tea rose (8)
18 Returning sweets created tension (8)
20 Noticed Hancock first in highly polished appearance (5)
23 Create order (7)
25 To sell old Spanish coin looks sound conclusion (7)
26 Empty tunnel going north before repairs (5)
27 English bureau might put up visiting American (9)
28 Foster new line for woodland management (8)
29 Encourage doctor after first struck off (4,2)

Down

1   Articulation apparent in G Sharp composition (8)
2   Dishes cooked in French kitchen possibly (7)
3   Could be threatening to do things differently (9)
5   Sinister urge? Just the opposite! (5-4,5)
6   Begin a fight (3,2)
7   Humour made confused Guildenstern back away (7)
8   Help donkey first (6)
9   Encounter poet appearing before profligate king (7,7)
16 Sober citizen briefly glimpsed attending a final farewell (9)
17 Best bun cut up and consumed (8)
19 Acrobatic fellow holding drink (7)
21 Summary of unfinished epic novel, for example (7)
22 Scratch around right at the back of the neck (6)
24 Solemn promise often made by taking these (5)

24

Across

1   Routine operation in the field ignoring the informer? (7,3,5)
9   Mountain range with peaks usually regarded as less steep (5)
10 River rose to become this? (9)
11 Places where parts are taken or removed? (8)
12 Base part of stalk aligns badly (6)
14 Government left in regret (4)
15 Slight change in direction aggrieves militant (10)
18 Get international body to support inclusion of German article (10)
19 Itemize record catalogue (4)
21 Motorists often the victims of these vices (6)
23 One who's usually blue if you're in the red (8)
25 Girl in back seat a Roman is involved with? (9)
26 Comic feast? (5)
27 A nasty complaint about station register (15)

Down

1   23, maybe, having a bash at self-defence (15)
2   Well-connected cosmopolitan so described (9)
3   On the spot, as Caesar might have been (2,4)
4   Get into the plot through this? (6,4)
5   Old socks for gardeners (4)
6   Idiotic change to shapeless top (8)
7   Fragrant smell from a European capital (5)
8   Military bases where the motorist can refuel (7,8)
13 Operation which may take place in gardens or 11 (10)
16 Travelling Italian tanner I upset (9)
17 Rotten part with exit on stage (4-4)
20 South African doctor in Lancaster, for example (6)
22 Accumulate a quantity (5)
24 Produced round cheese (4)

25

Across

1   Clothing acceptable in custody (6)
4   Whereby Roman locomotive runs on four lines (8)
10   With Angelo's backing, he'd be a Renaissance man (7)
11   Drink turned editor against family (7)
12   Preparing climber, perhaps, for different position (10)
13   Entrance with cross set back (4)
15   Spectator's father found accessory is included (7)
17   Authorize directions to count, for example (7)
19   Grey said to be one (7)
21   Scores against depleted team in Italy (7)
23   Some decide to send up eternal fall guy (4)
24   No words and no picture from this copier (10)
27   Boy takes in stray crane (7)
28   Deprecate mean measure (7)
29   Adventurous nightlife, we're told (8)
30   French artist's entry finally discarded (6)

Down

1   Possibly create dam to separate areas (9)
2   Told to name surrounding colour (7)
3   Mariner's joint craft (10)
5   Caesar felt Brutus' cut the most – this according to Antony (9)
6   Fish out relative (4)
7   Broadcast left-wing views here! (7)
8   Take part in a dire production of *The Lower Depths* (5)
9   Scottish 11?
14   Brings neat recipe for food (6-4)
16   One who splits hairs to get rid of unwelcome visitors? (9)
18   Big game hunter confounded somewhere in the south of England (9)
20   Rome, pre-Revolution, ruled by him (7)
22   Hustle using knave and king after ... (7)
23   ... a trick shuffle ... (5)
25   ... originally exposes all cards held individually (4)
26   11 briefly left in oven (4)

Across

1 Speed party (10)
6 Accountant and politician join clique (4)
10 Few passes for girls in these, observed Parker (7)
11 In for hairdo? Do just the opposite (7)
12 Get rid of bird nesting in flower (9)
13 Heavy poles pushed into the river (5)
14 Peer obtained part-time qualification (5)
15 Hastens in order to get directions in suburb (4,5)
17 Fertile region on large island (9)
20 One backed the French Prime Minister to get things moving (5)
21 Small girl ran round outside the pits (5)
23 A fight after prison porridge (9)
25 Appear to run away from man-eater in confusion (7)
26 Make clergy idle round here in France (7)
27 Healthy beginnings salute a new era (4)
28 Enter nice park to re-establish close relationship (10)

Down

1 Keen to hear this coming up the Severn? (5)
2 President has carte blanche for such drugstore philosophy (9)
3 Peter, for example, lacking final direction gets in with heretical teacher (14)
4 Will made to try tea blend (7)
5 He pours out music from his lyre (7)
7 A seed often found beneath the oak tree (5)
8 Will Scarlet go with this swashbukling figure? (9)
9 Belief in knowing where you're going before you get there (14)
14 Those who construct trains to carry royal passenger (9)
16 Former terrorists' son one caught in the blast (9)
18 Gold reset changes to become tough (7)
19 Bird flying up allowed to get small morsel (7)
22 Sewer unpicks 21 (5)
24 Subject of article I object to (5)

27

Across

1 Fugitive lacking direction for hiding place ... (6)
4 .... ran away and sank without trace (8)
10 Original painter who may have been self-taught (9)
11 No way royal stutterer can be made to broadcast (5)
12 One who would love to have lied about age, no doubt! (5)
13 End bit at the foot of a page (9)
14 They cared about changes made for television (7-3,4)
18 Sweet language from French blonde (7,7)
20 Animals in box, perhaps, discovered by this clipper (9)
22 Calm down after a fit of bad temper (5)
24 Record what might be said to a knocker (5)
25 Sends one invention born before of necessity (9)
26 Class reported too soon for once (8)
27 Hit and ran (6)

Down

1 Reprimand professional found in range (8)
2 Overheated friend loses partner (5)
3 Good Scottish publication has English introduction for tourists (5,4)
5 Vicar might call on book-keeper to perform these (8,6)
6 Ace of hearts could be first from the bottom (5)
7 Issue concealed microphone for someone dishing the dirt! (6,3)
8 Obscure old vessel taken into study (6)
9 Very light, perhaps, a sign of trouble (8,6)
15 One instrumental in signalling four out of 6 safe (9)
16 Rambling lecture sent up musical (9)
17 Emphasized importance to senior journalist (8)
19 By this means alone (6)
21 Eager to thrash out compromise (5)
23 Alarm gets you wide-awake (5)

28

Across

1 Pain from squeezing right inside tent (5)

4 Result of pile-up, in the main (9)

9 State a possible cause of 4 *Ac* (9)

10 Somewhere to drink in the vicinity (5)

11 Recognize South African instrument (6)

12 Singers start rehearsal with no score for new arrangement (8)

14 Trying to keep fit can be worrying (10)

16 Large fish in position to dive (4)

19 Reward returned to judge (4)

20 Reported naval movement observed keenly in the Middle East (5,5)

22 Carves out openings skiing enthusiasts may fall into! (8)

23 Performer, we hear, reads while playing (6)

26 Painter Edward valued highly (5)

27 Cutter once pulled from rock (9)

28 Committed old boy who lied about pistol (9)

29 Dandy with inflated opinion of himself? (5)

Down

1 Theatre company faces loss after Emu farce (9)

2 Part-time Devonian village blacksmith works at this (5)

3 Evaluate scenes in rehearsal (8)

4 Such laughter heard in restaurants round here? (4)

5 Grant only one involved unwittingly (10)

6 Bats may emerge from this wood (6)

7 Misplaced effort surrounding key evacuation (9)

8 'Yet each man — the thing he loves' *(Wilde)* (5)

13 Tax fools men in the street (10)

15 Three consecutive letters, say, totally at the heart of the matter (9)

17 Choose examination candidates for this process (9)

18 Do we encounter such characters in strange spheres? (8)

21 Pekinese companion has drink to follow (6)

22 Transport to depart with this on board? (5)

24 Sad confession before novice is sent out to indoctrinate (5)

25 Drug addiction first seen by detectives (4)

29

Across

1 Describing transport of City at a standstill (8)
6 Moody page went missing from domestic duty (6)
9 Return a map with an inset showing major canal (6)
10 Trap caught engineers back in shelled amphibian (8)
11 Poor accommodaton makes young ox grow old (8)
12 Walker initially lost sight of another (6)
13 Text detailed bonus offer (5)
14 Characteristic of mental disorder around in East (9)
17 If he's about, remain around ark! (9)
19 Carried away, perhaps, after a remarkable performance (5)
22 Singular French article that I got absorbed in (6)
23 One of four named in revelations (8)
24 Lead Greek character into great problems (8)
25 Criticize noted article I object to (6)
26 Head down having broken firm's first universal rule (6)
27 American soundly beats old players (8)

Down

2 Boisterous tea circle briefly upset citizen (7)
3 Great Dani may be misprint for this dramatic figure! (9)
4 Sparkling headgear often worn by ruler... (6)
5 ... who once mobilized support against fiery revolutionaries (9,6)
6 Proper name for peg, perhaps (8)
7 Urge disobedient child to go to fashionable University (7)
8 Founder of classes on the hill (9)
13 Surgeon takes credit for operation to cut out parasite (9)
15 Fluster a maiden awfully by being bossy (9)
16 Serge may be much in evidence (8)
18 Take off inside the limit at end of runway (7)
20 Count this before drinking, perhaps – his victims afterwards? (7)
21 Get angry when trains aren't working (6)

30

Beyond the Black-and-white Grid

At various points in the text, we have mentioned the fact that more complex crosswords exist – such as those that appear in the colour supplements of *The Observer* and *Sunday Times*. These puzzles, particularly the one by Jonathan Crowther ('AZED') in *The Observer*, develop traditions started by three famous crossword-setters, Torquemada, Afrit and Ximenes. (Ximenes – Derrick Macnutt – was responsible for laying down much of the 'ethical' basis of clue-writing and diagram construction in his book *Ximenes on the Art of the Crossword*.)

The most obvious difference between the so-called 'advanced' cryptic and the ordinary daily crossword is that the advanced variety uses a completely different style of diagram: the barred diagram. Instead of black squares, the divisions between solutions are marked on the grid with bars. The barred diagram usually contains fewer squares (12 x 12 as opposed to 15 x 15) but all of the squares are filled when the puzzle is completed. This gives the crossword a rather daunting appearance, although it should be pointed out that there are fewer 'unches' (unchecked squares) than in most conventional diagrams, thus giving the solver a greater chance of working out answers to some of the more diabolical clues – provided, of course, that the 'straightforward' ones have already been solved!

The level of vocabulary required to solve an advanced cryptic is such that a dictionary (*Chambers* is almost invariably recommended) is essential. Both solutions and clues can contain highly obscure words or archaic usages, although setters usually try to obey one of the golden Ximenean rules, whereby a difficult solution should have a (relatively) easy clue.

Advanced cryptics still contain most, if not all, of the devices that we have described in this book. However, many of the indications (of anagrams, for instance) are much more sophisticated, and the range of abbreviations and 'crosswordspeak' is also considerably more varied. In addition, these puzzles may employ a number of devices that we have not described, such as the composite anagram. With this device, the solution is a definition that, when anagrammatized with one or more elements derived from the clue, forms another of the words in the clue.

Such devices, as well as the many possible variations provided by special rubrics and unconventional diagrams, are beyond the scope of this book. Anyone wishing to explore these areas further can do no better than consult Don Manley's *Crossword Manual* (Chambers), which contains a detailed description of the features of advanced cryptics, together with a large number of sample puzzles.

Two-way Crossword Glossary

Beneath the veneer of natural language in a cryptic crossword clue lies a subtext of abbreviations and unconventional meaning that is the shared vocabulary of crossword-setters and solvers. Learning how to solve cryptic crosswords depends to a large extent on building up a familiarity with the range of possible abbreviations and meanings that can be denoted by certain words in the clues. It involves being aware, for instance, that while 'sailor' can be a literal synonym of 'mariner' or 'yachtsman', it is just as likely that it indicates AB (Able Seaman), OS (Ordinary Seaman), JACK or TAR. It may even be referring to a famous example such as DRAKE or NELSON.

A number of publications, some of which are recommended in **Further Reading and Contacts**, provide highly comprehensive lists of cryptic crossword vocabulary. Our own Glossary does not attempt to compete with these books; it is designed to assist with solving the puzzles in this book and – more importantly – as a general aid to developing awareness of the possible ambiguities that underlie an apparently innocent word or phrase. Remember that the words and phrases in a cryptic clue often translate into structural building blocks which are arranged to form the solution invited by the definitional element in the clue.

We have described this as a 'Two-way' Glossary, which means that if you look up SAILOR in the alphabetical listing you will find 'tar' as one of the equivalents, and that 'sailor' is there as one of the alternatives under TAR. Given the limited scope of the work, however, it was neither possible nor desirable to be absolutely consistent in this, nor to feature more than a glimpse of various literal synonyms of words commonly found in crossword clues. For example, the entry for TREE gives 'actor' (Sir Herbert Tree) and '*any example*'; the brief list of examples that follows this consists of short words that might be used as building blocks in the solution of a structural clue.

We have also tried to include in the Glossary a cross-section of vocabulary used to indicate the devices or instructional elements found in clues. Thus, under the entry ON can be found: '*indicates letter(s) above/below*' – showing that the word can represent an instruction to add one element in the clue to another to form the solution.

Finally, we have included some of the more common anagram indicators, which we have marked in the alphabetical listing with an asterisk.

Please note that we have deliberately omitted all full points from abbreviations and that we have not generally employed accents and apostrophes as these are invariably ignored within puzzle solutions.

A ace, adult, alpha, an, ante, argon, article, Austria, best, first (letter), first class, high class, I (= 1), key, note, one, per, vowel

AA abstainer, ack-ack, Alcoholics Anonymous, anti-aircraft, Automobile Association, flak, non-drinker, teetotal, TT

AB Able(-bodied) seaman, backward scholar, Jack, mariner, rating, sailor, tar

ABB abbess, abbey, abbot

ABANDONED* free, left

ABBESS Abb

ABBEY Abb

ABBOT Abb

ABE Lincoln (Abraham)

ABLE fit

ABLE(-BODIED) SEAMAN AB

ABOARD on board, *indicates letter(s) between 'SS'*

ABOUT* c, ca, circa, concerning, on, re, *indicates reversal of letters, letters surrounding*

ABOVE over, *indicates letter(s) positioned above*

ABSTAINERS AA, non-drinkers, teetotallers, TTs

AC account, air(crafts)man, alternating current, bill

ACADEMICIAN ARA, RA

ACC account(ant), accusative (case), bill

ACCEPTABLE OK, U

ACCOUNT ac, acc, bill, narrative, story, tale

ACCOUNTANT acc, CA

ACE A, best, card, champion, expert, I (= 1), master, one, pilot, service, top

ACK-ACK AA (anti-aircraft)

ACT(S) bill(s), play(s), turn(s)

ACTOR ham (poor actor), player, thespian, Tree

ACTORS cast

AD advertisement, anno Domini, notice, nowadays, poster, present

ADC aide, Aide de Camp

ADDER counter, snake, viper

ADD(ITION) PPS, PS, sum, *indicates letter(s) added*

ADJUST* order

ADM Admiral

ADMIRAL Adm, *any example:* Nelson, *etc.*

ADO* fuss

ADORE love

ADRIFT* cast away

ADVERTISEMENT ad, notice, poster

ADVICE tip

AFLOAT on board, *indicates letter(s) between 'SS'*

A FRENCH un, une

A GERMAN ein, eine, einer

AFFAIR amour, business

AFRESH* anew

AFTERNOON pm, post meridiem

AFTERTHOUGHT postscript, PPS, PS

AG silver

AGAIN re(-)

AGAINST anti, con, v, no, noes, versus, vs, *indicates letter(s) adjoining*

AGE era, eon, epoch, period, time

AGED old

AGENDA business

AGENT G-man, mole, rep, representative, spy,

AGENTS CIA, G-men, intelligence, MIV (= MI5), moles, spies

AGITATED* excited, stirred

AGITATOR* revolutionary, stirrer

AHEAD forward, in front, *indicates letter(s) preceding*

AHOY hail, hi, welcome

AI (= A1) best, capital, elite, excellent, first class, high class, sloth (ai)

AID assistance, help, tend

AIDE ADC, (Aide de Camp)

AIM end, goal, object

AIR appearance, bearing, display, element, look, mien, tune

AIRFORCE RAF, RFC

AIRMAN AC, flier/flyer, FO (Flight Officer), PO (Pilot Officer); oboist, trumpeter, *etc.*

AIRMEN RAF, Royal Air Force

AIR RAID PRECAUTIONS ARP

AIT island (small)

AL Alabama, Albania, aluminium, boy's name, Capone, gangster

A LA to the French

ALABAMA Al

ALBANIA AL

ALCOHOL *Any example:* brandy, gin, wine, *etc.*

ALCOHOLICS ANONYMOUS AA

ALDERMAN Ald

ALECTO Fury

ALIEN* ET, foreign, *any foreigner:* German, Slav, *etc.*

ALL completely, everything

ALL OVER THE PLACE* awry

ALL RIGHT OK, okay, U

ALLOW grant, let, permit

ALLY associate, Axis, friend, mate, pal

ALPHA A, first, IST (= 1st)

ALTERED* changed, reorganized

ALTERNATING CURRENT AC

ALTERNATIVE(LY) or

ALUMINIUM Al

ALWAYS e(v)er

AM American, backward scholar, be, early, exist, morning

AMATEUR A, L (learner), tyro, ham

AMBASSADOR diplomat, Excellency, HE

AMEN last word

AMERICA(N) Am, US, USA, Uncle Sam, Yank, Yankee,

AMERICAN SOLDIER GI

AMOK* chaotic

AMONG inter, *indicates hidden word, letters placed within word*

AMOUR affair, love, love affair

AMPUTATED cut, *indicates deletion of letter(s)*

AN a, article, I (= 1), if, one

ANCIENT archaic, Iago, old, *indicates obsolete spelling*

AND FRENCH et

AND OTHERS et al

ANEW* afresh, again

ANGER* ire, fury, rage

ANGLE corner, fish, L, point of view, turn

ANGLER fisherman

ANGRY* cross

ANIMAL beast, *any example:* bear, lion, seal, *etc.*

ANNO DOMINI AD

ANNOUNCEMENT ad, advert

ANON anonymous, soon, shortly, prolific poet

ANS (short) answer, reply

ANSWER ans, reply

ANT insect, (social) worker

ANTE a, before, pre(-)

ANTI against, con, v, versus, vs

ANTI-AIRCRAFT AA, ack-ack, flak

APE copy, primate

APPEAL O, Oh

APPEAR come out, emerge, issue

APPEARANCE air, bearing, look, mien

APPENDIX addition, app, *indicates additional letter(s)*

APPLICATION use

APPRENTICE L, learner, tyro

APRIL Apr, Apl, March past

APPROX(IMATE) about, c

AQ water

ARAMIS Musketeer

ARCH bridge, spanner

ARCHAIC ancient, old, once

ARCHED bowed

ARCHER bowman, bridge, Cupid, Dan, Eros, Hood, Tell

ARE exist

AREA locality, quarter, region, *any district:* EC, NE, *etc.*

ARGON A

ARID dry

ARIES heavenly, body, ram

ARISTOCRAT lord, noble, peer, *any example:* earl, duke, lady *etc.*

ARM branch, limb, member

ARMY host, soldiers, TA, *etc.*

ARP air raid precautions

AROUND* about, c, *indicates letter(s) surrounding*

ARRANGE* order, fix

ARRIVAL arr

ARRIVAL TIME birth, ETA

ARSENAL gunners, RA

ART article, boy's name, craft, cunning, painting, skill

ARTICLE a, an, art, the

ARTILLERY cannon, guns, RA, weapons

ARTIST painter, RA, *any example:* Bacon, Tiepolo, *etc.*

AS when

ASHEN pale, wan

ASK beg, O, Oh, plead, request

ASLEEP resting, *indicates letter(s) within* 'bed' *or* 'cot'

ASPECT bearing, look , mien

ASS dope, donkey, dupe

ASSEMBLY* company

ASSENT aye, nod

ASSESS rate, tax

ASSISTANCE aid, help

ASSESSMENT tax, value

ASSOCIATION Ass, Assoc

ASSOCIATE ally, pal

ASSUME don, put on

ASTRAY* awry

AT SEA* aboard, *indicates letter(s) within* 'SS' (steamship)

ATE consumed, dined, goddess

ATOMIC A (bomb)

AT HOME in, not out

AT UNIVERSITY up
ATHOS Musketeer
ATROPOS Fate
ATTACK offensive
ATTEMPT essay, try
ATTORNEY DA
ATTRIBUTE character
AU gold, to the French
AUDIENCE house
AUG August
AUGER awl, drill *(sounds like augur)*
AUGUR foretell, prophesy *(sounds like auger)*
AUGUST Aug, stately
AUNT Sally
AUSTRALIA Oz
AUSTRIA A
AUTO automatic, car
AUTOMOBILE ASSOCIATION AA
AUTHOR pen, writer, *any example:* Swift, Wells, *etc.*
AV avenue, average, bible (Authorised Version)
AVE avenue, average, hail, welcome
AVENUE av, avenue, road, way
AVERAGE ave, mean, medium, norm, par, standard
AVOID miss *(sounds like mis-)*
AWAY gone off, out, *indicates removal of letter(s)*
AWL drill, auger
AWKWARD* clumsy, gauche
AWRY* amok, astray
AY assent, yes

B bachelor, baron, Belgium, beta, bishop, black, book, born, bowled, boy, breadth, British, bye, extra, key, note
BA Bachelor of Arts, barium, degree, graduate, scholar
BACON artist, author, ham
BACHELOR B
BACHELOR OF ARTS BA
BACHELOR OF MEDICINE MB
BACK bet, support, second, stern *indicates reversal of letters*
BACKWARD SCHOLAR AB, AM
BACKWARDS *Indicates reversal of letters*
BAD* evil, off, wicked
BADLY* ill
BALL beamer, bouncer, dance, delivery, O,
BANGER car, firework, gun, sausage
BAR counter, obstacle, pub, save
BARD Shakespeare
BARIUM Ba
BARON aristocrat, B, joint, peer
BARONET Bart, Bt
BARREL cask, drum, part of gun
BART Baronet, Lionel
BASE METAL lead
BATTALION Bn
BATTERED* buffeted
BATTING in, not out
BB bed and breakfast, books, Boys' Brigade, Brigitte Bardot, very black/soft (pencil)

BC before Christ, British Columbia

BE am, exist, live

BEAK bill, judge, magistrate, master, nose, pecker, teacher

BEAM joist, light, ray

BEAMER ball, delivery

BEARING air, appearance, aspect, carriage, direction (N, E, S, W, NE, *etc.*), look, port, relation, *indicates containing letter(s) or support of letter(s) above*

BEAT best, lam, tan

BECK beckon, brook, rill, stream

BECKON beck

BED cot, flower bed

BED AND BREAKFAST B (and) B

BEE buzzer, drone, insect, worker

BEETLE insect, Volkswagen, VW

BEFORE ante, ere, pre(-)

BEFORE CHRIST BC

BEG ask, request, O, Oh, plead

BEGIN start, *indicates beginning of word*

BEGINNER deb, L, learner, novice, starter, tyro

BEHOLD Lo, see

BELG Belgium

BELGIUM B, Belg

BELIEVE credit

BELOW sub, under, *indicates letters placed below*

BEND bow, curve, S, U

BENT bowed, crooked, dishonest, grass

BESIEGE invest, *indicates letter(s) within a word*

BEST A, AI (= A1), ace, beat, champion, cream, worst

BET back, gamble

BETTING backing, odds, SP

BETA B, second (letter)

BETWEEN inter, *hidden word*

BIBLE AV, RV, NT, OT

BID call, try

BIG grand, huge, large, OS (outsize)

BIKE RACE TT (Tourist Trophy)

BILL ac(c), account, invoice, notice, poster, Will, William

BIRD flier, winger, *any example:* hen, rook, swift, *etc.*

BIRTH arrival time, nativity

BISHOP B, Bp, chessman, churchman, RR, piece on (chess) board

BISHOPRIC see, *any example:* Ely, *etc.*

BIT chewed, part, *indicates part of word*

BIZARRE* odd, strange

BK book

BL British Legion, British Leyland

BLACK B, BB, dark, inky, jet, sable

BLOOMER error, flower *(any example: daisy, pink, etc.)*, mistake

BLOOMING out

BLOW UP* erupt, explode, inflate

BLOWER phone, telephone, wind (player)

BLUE colour, Conservative, down, low, sad, Tory

BLUSH colour, redden

BM (British) Museum

BMA British Medical Association

BO body odour, holy tree

BOARD (company) directors, embark, food, keep, table

BOAT E, ship, SS, U, vessel, yacht

BOB bounce, hairstyle, s (shilling), sleigh, uncle

BOBBY copper, policeman, PC

BODY ODOUR BO

BOER South African

BOMB explosive device, *any example:* VI (= V1), *etc.*

BOOK b, bk, enter, log, reserve, tome, vol, volume

BOOKS bb, NT, OT

BORN b, n, nat, né, née

BOSS chief, head, stud

BOTHER* fuss

BOUGH arm, branch, limb

BOUNCE bob

BOUNCER ball, delivery

BOUNDARY edge, fence, four (IV), six (VI), wall

BOW bend, curve, obeisance, play (violin *etc.*), submit

BOWED arched, bent

BOWL dismiss, vessel

BOWLED b, delivered, out

BOWMAN archer, fiddler, Cupid, Eros, Hood, Tell, violinist

BOY lad, son, *any (usually shortened) example:* Al, Sam, Tom, *etc.*

BOYS' BRIGADE BB

BOX case, coffin, container, fight, spar

BOXER Chinese, dog, *any example:* Clay, Dempsey, *etc., or* heavyweight, flyweight, *etc.*

BP Bishop

BR branch, Brazil, bridge, Britain, British, British Rail, brother, brown, lines, railway, trains

BRA (female) support(er)

BRADMAN Don

BRAINS intelligence, nous

BRANCH arm, bough, Br, limb, member

BRAVE gallant, heroic, Red Indian

BRAVE MAN DFC, DFM, DSC, DSM, GC, hero, MC, VC

BRASS cash, money

BRAZIL BR

BREADTH b

BREAK* crack, pause, smash, *indicates letter(s) within word*

BREVE note

BREWED* distilled

BRIDGE br, arch, archer, card game, rest, spanner

BRIDGE PLAYERS N, S, E, W (partners)

BRIGITTE BARDOT BB

BRITAIN GB, UK

BRITISH Br

BRITISH COLUMBIA BC

BRITISH LEGION BL

BRITISH LEYLAND BL

BRITISH MEDICAL ASSOCIATION BMA

BRITISH MUSEUM BM

BRITISH RAIL BR

BRO brother

BROADCAST sew, spread

BROOK beck, flower, rill, rivulet, Sir Peter, stream, tolerate

BROTHER Br, Bro, Fra, friar, monk, sib, sibling

BROWN br, colour, tan

BRR shiver
BT baronet
BUCKLE* clip
BUFFETED* battered
BULLETS magazine
BURLINGTON HOUSE RA, Royal Academy
BURN char
BURNS chars, poet (Rabbie), Scottish flowers, runners, *etc.*
BURST* break, explode
BURY entomb, inter
BUSINESS affair, agenda, Co, company, firm
BUT object
BUTCH masculine
BUTLER RAB, man, servant
BUTTER goat, ram, person who hesitates
BUZZER bee
BY per, through
BYE b, extra, valediction

C 100, about, around, carbon, caught, celsius, cent, centigrade, century, chapter, circa, cold, Conservative, Cuba, hundred, key, note, large number, many, roughly, ton, Tory
CA about, calcium, California, (Chartered) Accountant, circa
CAB hansom, taxi, transport
CADMIUM Cd, colour
CALCIUM Ca
CALIFORNIA CA, Cal, Calif
CALL bid, dial, hail, hi, name, phone, ring, shout, telephone
CALLIOPE Muse
CAN is able, preserve, tin, vessel
CANADA CDN
CANVAS sail, tent
CAP hat, lid, top
CAPE cloak, Good Hope, Horn, head(land), ness, point
CAPITAL AI (= A1), chief, head, principal, upper case, *any example:* Paris, NY (New York), *etc.*
CAPONE Al, gangster
CAPS capitals, *indicates letters going above*
CAPTAIN Capt, leader, master, skipper, *any example:* Hornblower, *etc.*
CAPTIVE POW (prisoner of war), *indicates letter(s) within*
CAPTURE ensnare, net, trap, *indicates letter(s) within*
CAR auto, banger, carat, T, *any example:* Ford, MG, *etc.*
CARAT car
CARBON C
CARD humorous character, *any example:* Ace, Jack, King, Queen, Heart, Spade, *etc.*
CARD GAME *Any example:* bridge, solo, *etc.*
CARDS pack
CAREER course
CARE OF co
CARRIAGE bearing, port, trap, *any example:* hansom, phaeton, *etc.*
CARRY FORWARD cf
CARTOONIST *Any example:* Gilray, Low, *etc.*

CASE box, container, character, (law)suit, *any example:* acc(usative), nom(inative), voc(ative), *etc.*

CASH brass, money, tin

CASH ON DELIVERY cod

CASK barrel, hogshead, keg, tun

CAST actors, company, players, throw, toss

CASTLE chessman, chess piece, fortress, R, rook, stronghold

CAT cat o'nine tails, puss, punishment, tom, *any example:* lion, ounce, *etc.*

CATCH ensnare, fish, net, trap

CATTLE kine, neat, oxen

CAUGHT c, ct, dismissed, out, snagged, snared, trapped

CC county council, cricket club, cubic centimetre, two hundred

CD cadmium, Civil Defence, Corps Diplomatique, diplomats

CDN Canada

CE Church (of England), (Civil) Engineer

CELEBRITY VIP

CELSIUS C

CENT c, century, coin

CENTIGRADE C

CENTRAL key, *indicates the middle of a word*

CENTRAL HEATING ch

CENTRE middle, *indicates the middle of a word*

CENTS money

CENTRAL INTELLIGENCE AGENCY agents, CIA, intelligence, spies

CENTURY c, cent, hundred, ton

CF carry forward, compare, confer

CH central heating, chapter, child, China, church, Companion (of Honour), Switzerland

CHAMPION ace, best

CHANGE* variation

CHANGED* altered, reordered, reorganized

CHANNEL ISLANDS CI

CHAP chapter, fellow, gent, man, *any name:* Bill, Ted, *etc.*

CHAOTIC* disordered

CHAPTER c, ch, chap, section

CHA tea, *sounds like:* char

CHAR burn, cleaner, daily, do, domestic, home help, Mrs Mopp, tea

CHARACTER attribute, case, letter, personality, type

CHARGE ion, price, ward

CHARTERED ACCOUNTANT CA

CHE Guevara, revolutionary

CHEAT con, do, fiddle, rook

CHEF cook

CHIEF boss, capital, head, main, principal, *any example:* Geronimo, *etc.*

CHIEF OFFICER CO

CHESSMAN/PIECE bishop, castle, king, knight, man, pawn, queen, rook

CHILD ch, imp, issue, tot

CHILDBIRTH labour

CHILLY cold

CHINA Ch, dishes, orient, plates, service, *any example:* Dresden, *etc.*

CHINESE oriental, *any dynasty:* Ming, Tang *etc.*

CHRISTMAS present time

CHROMIUM Cr

CHROMOSOME X, Y

CHURCH CE, Ch, RC

CHURCHMAN abbe, curate, curé, DD, father, parson, prelate, priest, minister, Rev, *any office-holder:* (arch)bishop, dean, *etc.*

CHURCH OF ENGLAND CE

CI Channel Islands

CIA agents, Central Intelligence Agency, intelligence, spies

CID detectives, Spanish hero, Yard

CIPHER nil, nought, nothing, O, zero

CIRCA about, around, c, ca

CIRCLE disc, O, ring, round, zero

CIRCUIT O, ring

CIT cited, citizen

CITED cit

CITIZEN cit

CITY EC, ECI (= EC1), *any example:* Ely, Rome, *etc.*

CIVIL DEFENCE ARP, CD

CIVIL ENGINEER CE

CIVIL SERVICE CS

CL 150, chlorine

CLASP hold, *indicates letter(s) held*

CLASS A, B, *etc.*, form, order, rank, U

CLASSIC Derby, National, Oaks, *indicates Latin, Greek term*

CLASSICAL *Relates to Latin, Greek civilization*

CLEANER char, home help

CLERGY churchmen, cloth

CLERGYMAN abbé, curate, curé, DD, father, parson, prelate, priest, minister, Rev, *any office-holder:* (arch)bishop, dean, *etc.*

CLINK gaol, jail

CLIO Muse

CLIP cut, *indicates letter(s) removed*

CLOAK cape, manteau

CLOTH churchmen, clergy, priests, *any material:* drill, serge, *etc.*

CLOTHO Fate

CLUB card, mace, *any golf club:* driver, iron, niblick, wedge, *etc.*, *any institution:* Athenaeum, MCC, RAC, Tottenham, Villa, *etc.*

CLUE key

CLUSTER group, set

CO business, care of, cobalt, Colombia, Colorado, Commanding Officer, company, county, firm

COACH instruct, train, trainer, transport

COBALT Co

COCKNEY *Indicates imitation of Cockney pronunciation: dropped aitch, etc.*

COD cash on delivery, fish

COIN *Any example:* cent, penny (p, d), quarter, nickel, shilling, *etc.*

COINS currency, *plurals of above*

COL Colonel, Colorado, column, officer, pass, neck, soldier

COLD brr, c, chilly, frigid, icy

COLLAPSE* fall

COLLEGE school, *any example:* Eton, King's, New, *etc.*

COLONEL Col, officer

COLOMBIA CO

COLORADO CO, Col

COLOUR(S) blush, flag, hue, standard *any colour:* red, blue, *etc.*

COLUMN col

COME BACK return, *indicates letter reversal*

COME OUT* appear, emerge, issue

COME TO arrive, *indicates letter(s) joining*

COME UP TO ascend, *indicates letter(s) read backwards*

COMMAND instruct, order

COMMANDING OFFICER CO

COMMON park(land), *any example:* Tooting, Wandsworth, *etc., indicates slang usage*

COMMON MARKET E(E)C

COMMONS (HOUSE OF) House

COMMUNIST Ivan, red, Russian *(though less frequent now)*

COMMUNITY E(E)C

COMPANION mate, pal, CH (of Honour)

COMPANY assembly, business, cast, co, firm, soldiers, two

COMPARE cf

COMPLICATED* difficult, hard, tough

COMPOSE* write

COMPOSER writer, *any example:* Britten, Ireland, *etc.*

COMPOSITION* essay, exercise

CON against, anti, cheat, Conservative, do, fiddle, party, politician, study, Tory, trick, versus, v, vs, with Italian

CONCEALED hidden, *indicates hidden word or letter(s) placed within word*

CONCERNING about, approx(imate), c, on, over, re

CONCLUSION end, *indicates last letter(s) of word*

CONCOCTION* mixture

CONFER cf

CONFRONT face

CONFUSED* fuddled, muddled

CONSECRATED BREAD / WAFER host

CONSERVATIVE blue, C, Con, party, politician, Tory

CONSTABULARY force, police

CONSTANT firm, Lambert, *any physical constant:* pi, *etc.*

CONSTRUCT* fabricate, make, produce

CONSUMED ate, dined

CONTAIN hold, *indicates letters held*

CONTAINER *Any example:* box, case, tin, vat, *etc.*

CONTEST match, test

CONTINENT clean, *any example:* Asia, Australia, *etc.*

CONTRIVE* engineer

CONVERSE talk, *indicates opposite*

COOK* chef, fiddle, explorer, *any method:* boil, fry, grill, stew, *etc.*

COP bobby, copper, policeman, PC, peeler

COPPER bobby, colour, cop, Cu, PC, peeler, penny (p, d), policeman

CORNER angle, turn

CORNET ice (cream), musical instrument

CORP Corporal

CORPORAL Corp, NCO, non-commissioned officer, Nym

CORPS DIPLOMATIQUE CD

CORRECT* alter, amend, emend, OK, right

COS cosine, island, lettuce

COSTA RICA CR

COT bed, cottage, house

COTTAGE cot, house

COUNT Dracula, earl, nobleman, number, tell

COUNTER adder, bar

COUNTRY rural, rustic, *any example:* Cuba, UK, US, *etc.*

COUNTY Co, *any example:* Avon, Beds, Mayo, Yorks, *etc.*

COUPLE pair, pr, two, *indicates doubling letter, syllable*

COURSE career, current, direction (N, S, E, W, NE, *etc.*), *any food course* dessert, pasta, soup, starters, *etc.*

COW frighten, lower, neat

CPL Corporal, non-commissioned officer

CR chromium, Costa Rica, credit

CRAFT art (*any example:* pottery, *etc.*), boat (*any example:* skiff, ship, *etc.*)

CRAFTSMAN artisan, sailor

CRAZY* mad

CREAM best, flower, upper class

CREDIT believe, cr, tick

CREW eight, oarsmen, rowers, scullers

CRICKET CLUB CC, MCC

CRICKET SIDE eleven, leg, off, on, XI

CRIME sin, tort, *any example:* murder, theft, *etc.*

CRIMINAL bad, *any type:* fence, thief, *etc.*

CRITICISM flak

CROOKED* bent, dishonest

CROSS* angry, enraged, frustrated, go over, hybrid, irate, X

CROWD mass, mob, *indicates a large number:* C, D, M, *etc.*

CRY greet, weep

CS Civil Service, (poison) gas

CT caught

CU copper

CUBA C

CUBIC CENTIMETRE cc

CUPID archer, bowman, Eros, love

CUR dog

CURRENCY coins, notes, *any example:* dollars, lira, yen, *etc.*

CURTAILED cut, shortened, *indicates letter(s) removed*

CURRENT AC, course, DC, modern, river, up-to-date

CURVE bend, bow

CUSTOM practice, usage, use

CUT clip(ped), hack(ed), ignore(d), lop(ped), *indicates letter(s) removed*

CWT hundredweight

CYPHER nil, nought, nothing, O, zero

CZ Czechoslovakia

CZECHOSLOVAKIA CZ

D 500, copper, daughter, day, dead, delta, deuterium, died, down, five hundred, Germany, key, late, many, note, (old) penny

DA District Attorney, (American) lawman

DAB expert, fish, master, pro, star, touch

DAD father, Fr, generator, old man, pa, pop

DAI Welshman

DAILY char, each day, home help, *any newspaper: Times, etc.*

DAN Archer, Cupid

DANCE* ball, measure, *any example: hop, twist, etc.*

DANDY beau, fop

DAUGHTER d, dtr, girl, issue, offspring

DAM barrier, mother, stop up

DAY d, *any day or abbreviation: Mon, Wed, Sun, etc.*

DC current, direct current, District Commissioner, District of Columbia

DD churchman, divine, Doctor of Divinity, theologian, tuppence, two pence

DE (DE LA, DU, DES) of the French

DEAD d, dec, ex, late, over, sea

DEAN Inge, religious man

DEAR duck, expensive, love

DEB beginner, debutante, girl, L, novice, one coming out

DEBT IOU

DEBTOR dr

DEBUTANTE beginner, deb, girl, L, novice, one coming out

DEC deceased, December, declared, last month, ult

DECEMBER Dec, last month

DECLARED dec

DECORATION honour, order, ornament, *any example:* MC, MBE, OBE, *etc.*

DEE river, *indicates letter* 'd'

DEEP sea

DEFENCE ARP, CD

DEGREE measure, standard, *any academic degree:* BA, MA, *etc.*

DEKKO look

DELAY hesitation

DELIVERED born, bowled

DELIVERIES balls, beamers, bouncers, overs

DELIVERY ball, beamer, birth, bouncer

DELTA D

DEN lair, retreat, study

DENOMINATION CE, RC

DEPARTMENT dept

DEPRESSED blue, down, sad

DESERTER rat

DESIGN* blueprint, intent, plan

DESIRE yen

DESSERT course, sweet

DETECTIVES CID, FBI, Feds, G-men, Yard

DEUTERIUM D

DEVOUT holy, pi, pious, religious

DEXTER right(-handed), Ted

DH Lawrence

DI 501, Diana, (small) girl, Princess

DIAL call, face, O, phone, ring, telephone

DIAMONDS ice

DIANA Di, goddess

DIED d, ex, late, ob

DIFFERENT* other

DIFFICULT* hard

DIG excavate, understand

DIGIT excavate (it), finger, number

DIMINUTIVE small, *indicates abbreviated form of name, etc.*

DIN dinner, noise, row, uproar

DINED ate, fed

DINNER din, meal

DIPLOMAT(S) ambassador, CD, Corps Diplomatique, HE

DIRECT CURRENT DC

DIRECTION N, S, E, W, NE, *etc.*, course, instruction, l(eft), r(ight), route, way

DIRECTORS board, dirs

DIS Erebus, Hades, Hell, pit, Pluto, Underworld

DISARRAY* disorder, mess

DISAPPROVE object

DISC circle, EP, LP, O, record

DISFIGURE* mar

DISHEARTENED down, *indicates letter(s) removed from centre of word*

DISHES china, plates

DISMISS bowl

DISMISSED fired, *any cricket dismissal:* b(owled), c(aught), st(umped), *etc.*

DISORGANIZED* haphazard, messy

DISORDERED* chaotic

DISPLAY air, show

DISTANCE measure(ment), *any example:* ft, in, mile, *etc.*

DISTILLED* brewed

DISTRICT ATTORNEY DA

DISTRICT COMMISSIONER DC

DISTURBED* troubled

DITTO do, same

DIVINE DD

DN down

DO char, cheat, con, ditto, make, note, party, rook, same, swindle

DOC doctor

DOCTOR doc, Dr, GP, MB, MD, MO, vet

DOCTOR OF DIVINITY DD

DOCUMENT(S) deed(s), ms, mss

DODO extinct creature, old bird

DO(H) note

DOG cur, follow, pup, tail, *any breed:* alsatian, peke, *etc.*, *any famous example:* Pluto, *etc.*

DOLLAR(S) S(s), currency, money

DOMESTIC char

DON assume, Bradman, nobleman, put on, river, Spaniard

DONE over, U

DOORWAY entrance

DOPE ass, drug, fool

DOSSIER file

DOT point

DOWN blue, d, depressed, dn, fluff, low, sad, swallow, *indicates reversal of letters in Down clue*

DOZ dozen

DOZE nod, kip, sleep

DOZEN doz, twelve, XII

DR Doctor

DRACULA Count

DRILL auger, bore, cloth, exercise, material

DRINK imbibe, nip, pint, tot, *any example:* ale, beer, gin, rum, *etc.*

DRIVER (golf) club, motorist

DROOP flag

DROP fall, tear, *indicates letter(s) deleted*

DRUG narcotic, *any example:* hash, hemp, grass, LSD, *etc.*

DRUM barrel

DRUNK(EN)* tipsy

DRY arid, sec, TT

DU of the French

DUCK dear, love, nil, nought, O, zero, *any example:* mallard, *etc.*

DUKE D

DUTCH wife

DUTCHMAN Hans

E bearing, bridge player, course, direction, East(ern), energy, English, key, note, orient(al), partner, point, quarter, Spain, vowel

EA each, per

EACH ea, per

EACH DAY daily

EARL Count, noble, peer

EARTH element

EASEL (artistic) support

EAST E, bearing, course, direction, Orient, point, quarter

EAST END EC

EASTERN oriental

EAST EUROPEAN *Any example:* Czech, Lett, Pole, *etc.*

EASTERN RULER *Any example:* Aga, emir, sultan, *etc.*

EC(I) (= EC1) City, East End

ECCENTRIC* odd, strange

ECO English Chamber Orchestra

ED editor, Edward, (top) journalist, Ted

EDITION ed, issue, number

EDITOR ed

EDWARD Ed, Lear, king (ER)

E(E)C community, (European) Common Market, international organization, market

EER always (poetic), ever

EG for example, for instance

EGG encourage, O, ovum, spur, urge

EGO for example none, personality, self

EGYPTIAN GOD(DESS) Isis, Ra

EIGHT crew, oarsmen

EL the Spanish, *indicates the letter* 'l'

ELEMENT air, earth, fire, water, *any chemical element:* C (carbon), fe (iron), *etc.*

ELEVEN (cricket) side, (football) team, XI

ELI priest

ELITE AI (= A1), flower, pick

ELL measure, length

ELY city, see

EM (printer's) measure, them, *indicates the letter* 'm'

EMBARK board

EMBRACE hug, *indicates letter(s) contained within a word*

EMEND* correct

EMERGE come out

EMIT issue
EMPEROR Emp, moth, penguin
EMPTY vacant, *indicates 'O'*
inserted
EN (printer's) measure, *indicates*
the letter 'n'
ENC enclosure
ENCHANT entrance, transport
ENCLOSE pen, fence, *indicates*
letter(s) within a word
ENCLOSURE enc, pen, pound,
indicates letter(s) within a word
ENCOURAGE egg
END aim, conclusion, finish, goal,
fin in France, object, *indicates end*
of word
ENDED over
ENERGY E, erg, force, go
ENERGY UNIT erg
ENG engineer, England, English
ENGINEER* CE, contrive, eng,
RE, sapper
ENGLAND/ENGLISH E, Eng
ENGLISH CHAMBER
ORCHESTRA ECO
ENSIGN flag, standard (bearer)
ENSNARE* capture, catch, net,
trap, *indicates (rearranged) letters*
inside another word
ENTER book, go in, log, record,
indicate(s) letters entering a word
ENTOMB bury, inter, *indicates*
letter(s) buried within a word
ENTRANCE doorway, enchant,
gateway, transport
ENTRY record, *indicates letter(s)*
entering a word
EP disc, epistle, extended play, record
EPISTLE ep

EPOCH age, era
EQUAL par
ER hesitation, Queen
ERA age, time
ERATO Muse
ERE before
EREBUS Dis, Hades, Hell, Pluto,
pit, Underworld
ERG energy unit
ERGO so, therefore
ERIC boy, gradually, little by little
(book title)
ERICA girl, heath, heather
ERR* sin, stray, wander
ERROR* bloomer
ERUPT* blow up, explode
ES(S) *Indicates the letter* 's'
ESSAY attempt, composition, try
ESSAYIST trier, *any example:*
Lamb (Elia), *etc.*
ESTIMATED TIME OF
ARRIVAL ETA
ET alien, and French, extra terrestrial
ETA arrival time, estimated time of
arrival
ET AL and others
ETC etcetera
ETCETERA etc
EUROPEAN *Any example:* Italian,
Swiss, *etc.*
EUROPEAN ECONOMIC
COMMUNITY Common
Market, EC, EEC, international
organization
EUTERPE Muse
EVEN evening (poetic), level, tie
EVENING eve, even, levelling,
tying
EVER eer

EVIL bad, sin(ful), wicked
EWE sheep
EWER jug
EX dead, former (husband, wife), from, late, old, once, out of, *indicating the letter* 'x'
EXAMINATION exam, oral, trial test, viva
EXAMINE con, read, study, try, test
EXAMPLE eg, model
EXCAVATE dig
EXCELLENT AI (= A1), first class
EXCELLENCY ambassador, HE
EXCITED* agitated, stirred, up
EXCLAMATION ah, aha, bah, eh, fie, O, oh, ooh, ouch, hey, hi, pah, pooh, tut, phew, ugh, *etc.*
EXE river
EXERCISE composition, drill, PE, PT, test
EXIST(S) am, are, be, is
EXPENSIVE dear
EXPERT ace, dab, master, pro, star
EXPLODE* blow up, erupt
EXPLORER *Any example:* Cook, Polo, *etc.*
EXPLOSIVE* HE, TNT
EXPLOSIVE DEVICE bomb, *any example:* A, VI (= V1), *etc.*
EXTENDED PLAY EP
EXTINCT dead (as a dodo), ex
EXTRA b(ye), l(eg) b(ye), w(ide)
EXTRA LARGE OS, outsize
EXTRA-TERRESTRIAL ET
EXTRAORDINARY* strange
EXTREME last, outer, *indicates first and last letters*
EYE look, looker, viewer
EYESORE stye

F fahrenheit, fathom, fellow, female, feminine, fluorine, folio, forte, France, French, Friday, key, loud, noisy, note
FA fah, Fanny Adams, Football Association, note, nothing
FABRIC material, *any example:* crepe, net, nylon, *etc.*
FABRICATE* construct, make
FACE confront, dial, mug
FACTORY plant
FAH fa, note
FAHRENHEIT F
FAIL plough
FAIRY peri
FALSE* untrue
FANNY ADAMS FA
FASHION* make, ton
FASHIONABLE in, U
FAST firm, fleet, Lent, quick
FATES spinners, Atropos, Clotho, Lachesis
FATHER dad, Fr, Fra, generate, generator, old man, pa, pop, sire
FATHERLAND Germany
FATHERS pas, pops
FATHOM f, understand
FAVOURITE pet
FAWKES guy
FBI detectives, feds, G-men
FE iron, further education
FEB February
FEBRUARY Feb
FEDS detectives, FBI, G-men
FEE pay, salary, wage

FELLOW boy, chap, don, F, FRS, gent, guy, man, *indicates man's name*

FEMALE f, feminine, hen, she

FEMININE f, female

FENCE boundary, pale, receiver

FETE do, party

FEW *Indicates Roman numerals up to ten:* I, II, IV, V, *etc.*

FF fast forward, folios, fortissimo, very loud

FIDDLE* con, cook, (play) violin

FIELDER *Any position:* gully, mid-on, third man, *etc.*

FIFTEEN side, team, XV

FIFTY half ton, L

FILE dossier, line

FIN end in France

FINAL(LY) last, ult, ultimate, *indicates word-ending*

FINGER digit, limb

FINISH close, end

FIRE element, sack

FIREWORK banger

FIRM business, Co, company, constant, fast, fixed

FIRST A, Alpha, I (= 1), IST (=1st), leading, top, winner, *indicates first letter(s) of word*

FIRST CLASS A, AI (= A1), ace, excellent, top, star

FISH(ES) angle, catch, school, swimmers, *any example:* cod, id, ide, ling, perch, ray, *etc.*

FISHERMAN angler, Peter

FIT* able, match, sound, spasm, suit

FIVE V

FIVE HUNDRED D

FIVE POUND (NOTE) fiver, VL

FIVER five pound (note)

FIX arrange

FIXED* firm

FLAG droop, ensign, iris, jack, standard, stone

FLAK AA, anti-aircraft, criticism

FLEET fast, gaol, navy, quick, RN, Royal Navy, ships

FLOWER bloomer, cream, pick, river *(plus any example)*, runner, *any example of flowers:* arum, iris, rose, *etc.*

FLUFF down

FLUORINE F

FO airman, Flight Officer, folio, Foreign Office

FOLIO(S) f, fo, ff

FOLLOW dog

FOOD board, *any example:* meat, pasta, *etc.*

FOOL ass, dope, sap

FOOTBALL ASSOCIATION FA

FOR pro

FORCE* energy, g(ravity), make, *any services:* RAF, RN, *etc.*

FORD car, Harrison, Henry, T

FOR EXAMPLE eg, for instance, say

FOR INSTANCE eg, for example, say

FOREIGN OFFICE FO

FOREIGNER *Any example:* Dane, Swiss, *etc.*

FORM* class

FORMER ex, late, old

FORTE f, loud, noisy

FORTISSIMO ff, noisy, very loud, very noisy

FORTRESS castle
FORTY XL
FORWARD ahead, hooker, prop, lock
FOUL rank
FOUR boundary, IV, quartet
FOURTH quarter
FR dad, father, France, French
FRA dad, father
FRANCE F, Fr, *indicates French word*
FREE* abandoned, liberal, liberated, no charge, rid
FRENCH F, Fr, *indicates French word*
FRENCHMAN M
FRENCHMEN MM
FRENZIED* mad
FRESH* new
FRIAR brother, fr,
FRIDAY F, Fri
FRIEND ally, mate, pal
FRIGID cold
FROM* ex, out of
FRONT van, *indicates beginning of word*
FRUSTRATE(D)* cross
FT feet, foot
FUDDLED* confused
FURIES Alecto, Megaera, Tisiphone
FUSS* ado

G gee, George, girl, gramme, gravity, key, note
GA Georgia

GAG joke, silence(r)
GAL girl
GALLERY gods, Tate
GAMBLE bet, dice, game, wager
GAME bet, dice, gamble, wager, *any example:* rugby (RU), *etc.*
GANGLAND underworld
GANGSTER Al (Capone), hood, mobster
GAOL clink, jug, stir, *any example:* Fleet, Reading, *etc.*
GARDEN (OF ENGLAND) Kent
GAS (POISON) CS
GAT(LING) gun, pistol
GATE entrance, wicket
GATEWAY entrance, port
GAUGE measure
GB (Great) Britain
GEE *Indicates the letter* 'g'
GEE-GEE gg, horse, mount, nag
GEM rock, (precious) stone, *any example:* agate, opal, ruby, *etc.*
GEN General, info, information, intelligence, lowdown
GENERAL Gen, universal, *any example:* Grant, Lee, *etc.*
GENERATE* father
GENERATOR dad, father, pa, pop
GENEROUS liberal
GENT(LEMAN) chap, fellow, Mr, Sir
GEO George
GEORGE G, Geo, king
GEORGIA Ga, girl
GERMAN D, *indicates German word:* das, der, die, Herr, Frau Graf, *etc.*
GERMANY D, Fatherland
GESTAPO SS

GG gee-gee, horse, mount, nag

GHOST shade, spirit

GI (American) soldier, Private

GIN drink, trap

GIRL daughter, deb, g, gal, miss, *any name:* Ann, Ella, Rose, *etc.*

GK Greek

GLAD happy, jolly

G-MEN FBI, Feds

GO energy, leave, turn, work, *indicates letter(s) leaving*

GO FIRST lead, *indicates placement of letter(s) initially*

GO IN enter, *indicates placement of letter(s) inside a word*

GOAL aim, end, score

GOD/GODDESS *Any example:* Ate, Isis, Mercury, Ra, *etc.*

GODS gallery

GOLD Au, colour, or

GONE left

GONG medal

GOOD OK, okay

GOOD HOPE cape

GOOD MAN S, Saint, St

GP doctor, group, medical man

GPO Post Office

GR grain, gramme, great, Greece, Greek, King George

GRADE Lew, quality, rank

GRADUALLY Eric *(book title)*, litle by little

GRADUATE BA, BSc, DSc, MA, *etc.*

GRAIN gr

GRAMME g, gr

GRAND great, K, M, piano, thousand

GRANITE rock, stone

GRANT allow, General

GRASS drug, inform, shop, sing, *any example:* bent, *etc.*

GRAVITY G, seriousness, weight

GRAVE INSCRIPTION RIP

GREAT gr, grand, gt

GREAT BRITAIN GB, UK

GREAT NUMBER host, *indicates large numeral:* C, D, M, *etc.*

GREECE Gr

GREEK Gk, Gr

GREEK LETTER *Any example:* beta, delta, mu, omega, pi, xi, *etc.*

GREET cry, hail

GRILL* cook, question

GRIP hold, *indicates letter(s) within a word*

GROUP* cluster, gp, set

GUEVARA Che

GUIDE lead, manual

GUN banger, gat

GUN, PART OF *Any part:* barrel, *etc.*

GUNNERS arsenal, RA, Royal Artillery

GUNPOWDER HE, TNT

GUNS artillery, gats

GUY Fawkes, fellow, rope, *any (American) name:* Elmer, Hank, *etc.*

GYPSY nomad, wanderer

H hard, height, Henry, hospital, hot, hour, house, Hungary, hydrogen

HA expression of surprise, Horse Artillery, laugh

HADES Dis, Erebus, Hell, pit, Pluto, Underworld

HAIL ave, ahoy, greet, hi, ho, welcome

HAIRSTYLE *Any example:* bob, perm, *etc.*

HAL Harry, Henry

HALF TON fifty

HALLO hi, ho

HAM bacon, (poor) actor

HANSOM carriage

HAND pass, worker

HAPHAZARD* disorganized, messy

HAPPY glad, jolly

HARBOUR port, *indicates letter(s) held within word or hidden word*

HARD* difficult, h

HARD WATER ice

HARRISON Ford, Rex

HARRY* Hal, Henry, worry

HAS bears

HASH* drug, mess

HAT cap, lid, top, *any example:* bowler, tile, *etc.*

HAVE own

HAYWIRE* mad

HE ambassador, helium, high explosive, His Eminence, (His) Excellency, male, man

HEAD boss, cape, capital, ness, pate, point, *indicates start of word*

HEADLAND cape, ness

HEADQUARTERS HQ

HEAPS lots, *indicates large numeral:* D, M, *etc.*

HEAR(D) *Indicates word(s) sound like something else*

HEART centre, *indicates middle of a word*

HEATH erica, Ted

HEATHER erica, girl, ling

HEAVENLY BODY planet, star, sun, sign of the zodiac, *any examples:* Aries, Mars, Venus, Virgo, *etc.*

HECK hell

HEED list, listen

HEIGHT h, ht

HELIUM He

HELL Dis, Erebus, Hades, heck, pit, Pluto, Underworld

HELLO hi, ho

HEMP drug, rope

HEN female

HENRY Ford, H, Hal, Harry

HESITATION delay, er, um

HER she (object), woman

HERMES Mercury

HERO brave man, DFC, DFM, DSC, DSM, GC, MC, VC

HG Mercury

HI hallo, hello

HIDE conceal, pelt, skin, *indicates hidden word, letter(s) inside word*

HIGGLEDY-PIGGLEDY* random

HIGH CLASS A, AI (= A1), U

HIGH EXPLOSIVE HE

HIGH SPEED TRAIN HST

HIGH TENSION HT

HIGHWAY M(I = 1), rd, road

HILL tor

HIM he (object), man

HINT tip

HIRE-PURCHASE HP, never-never

HIS EMINENCE HE
HIS EXCELLENCY HE
HIS/HER MAJESTY HM
HIT lam(med), rap(ped), strike (stricken, struck), tap(ped)
HITCHED married, wed
HM Her/His Majesty, King, Queen
HO hallo, hello, Home Office, house
HOLD(S) *Indicates letter(s) contained in a word*
HOLD UP rob, *indicates letters contained upside-down*
HOLLAND linen, NL
HOLY MAN S, Saint, St
HOLY TREE bo
HOME in
HOME HELP char, cleaner, daily
HOME OFFICE HO
HOME COUNTIES SE
HONOUR decoration, order, *any example:* CH, OBE, OM, *etc.*
HOOD bowman, gangster, Robin
HOOKER forward
HORSE gee-gee, gg, mount, nag, *any breed:* arab, *etc.*
HORSE ARTILLERY HA
HORSEPOWER hp
HOSPITAL H
HOST army, consecrated bread/wafer
HOT h, stolen
HOTCHPOTCH mess
HOUR h, hr
HOUSE audience, Commons, cot, cottage, h, ho, Lords
HP hire-purchase, horsepower, never-never, sauce
HQ headquarters

HR hour
HST high speed train
HT high tension
HUE colour, *any example:* red, *etc.*
HUG embrace, *indicates letter(s) within a word*
HUGE big, OS (outsize)
HUMOROUS CHARACTER card
HUNDRED C, century, land area, ton
HUNDREDWEIGHT cwt, measure
HUNGARY H
HUSH sh
HYBRID* cross
HYDROGEN H

I a, ace, an, iodine, island, Italy, me, one (= 1), single, vowel
I AM Im (= I'm)
IAN Scot(sman), *indicates Scottish word*
IC in charge (of)
ICE cornet, *etc.*, diamonds, hard water, reserve
ICELAND IS
ICY cold
ID fish, I had/I would (I'd), instinct, personality, self
IDA girl, mountain
IDE fish
IDLENESS sloth
IE that is, that's
IF an, provided
I HAD Id (= I'd)
II eleven, side, team
IL Illinois, the Italian

ILL* bad(ly), I will (= I'll), illustrated, not well, sick
ILLINOIS Ill
ILLUSTRATED ill
IM I am (= I'm)
IMBIBE drink
IMP (mischievous) child, little devil, rascal, rogue, scamp
IMPORTANT key, material
IMPORTANCE weight, moment
IN (at) home, batting, fashionable, Indiana, inch, inside, playing, not out, *indicates letters within a word*
IN CHARGE (OF) ic, over
IN COURT up
IN FRONT ahead, forward, *indicates letter(s) preceding*
INCH in, island, length, measure, move slowly
INCOHERENT* jumbled
INDEX list
INFERNO Underworld
INFO gen, information
INFORM grass, shop, sing
INFORMATION gen, info
INGE Dean, religious man
INITIAL(LY) *Indicates first letter(s) of word(s)*
INN PH, pub, tavern
INSECT *Any example:* ant, bee, fly, gnat, tsetse, wasp, *etc.*
INSIDE in, within, *indicates letter(s) within a word*
INST instant, this month
INSTANCE eg
INSTANT inst
INSTINCT id

INSTRUCT command, order, teach, train
INSTRUCTION direction
INTELLIGENCE brains, CIA, gen, IQ, MIV, spies
INTER between, bury, entomb, *indicates letter(s) within a word*
INTERNATIONAL ORGANIZATION E(E)C, UN, UNO, *etc.*
INVEST besiege, *indicates letter(s) within a word*
INVOICE bill
IO joy, ten (10 = IO)
IODINE I
IOM (Isle of) Man
ION charge
IOU(S) debt(s)
IQ intelligence (quotient)
IR iridium
IRATE* cross
IRE anger, Ireland, rage
IRELAND composer, Eire, emerald isle, Ire
IRIDIUM Ir
IRIS flag, flower, pupil
IRISHMAN Paddy, Pat
IRON club, Fe, press
IS exists, Iceland, island, Isaiah
IS ABLE can
ISAIAH Is
ISIS goddess, Thames
ISLAND I, Is, ait, inch, man, *any example:* Cos, IOM, *etc.*
ISLE (OF MAN) IOM
ISM theory
ISSUE child, come out, daughter, edition, emit, offspring, publish, son

IST (= 1ST) alpha

IT Italian, Italy, SA, sex appeal, (the) thing, vermouth

ITALIAN It, vermouth, *indicates Italian word*

ITALY I, It

IV four

IVAN communist, Russian

I WILL Ill (= I'll)

I WOULD Id (= I'd)

IX nine

J Jack, Japan, jay, judge, justice, knave

JACK AB, card, flag, J, John, knave, lift, mariner, rating, sailor, tar

JAN girl's/boy's name, January

JANUARY Jan

JAPAN J, lacquer, orient, varnish

JAPANESE oriental

JAY bird, *indicates the letter* 'j'

JE I in Paris/France

JO little woman

JOB post

JOCK Scot(sman), *indicates Scottish word*

JOG remind, trot

JOHN boy, Jack

JOINT baron, *any example:* ankle, hip, knee, *etc.*

JOIST beam

JOKE gag

JOLLY happy, marine, RM

JOURNALIST ed

JOY girl, Io

JP Justice (of the Peace), magistrate

JUDGE beak, J, magistrate, trier, try

JUG ewer, gaol

JUL July

JULY girl, Jul

JUMBLE(D)* incoherent, mix(ed) up

JUMP leap, spring, start, vault

JUMPER pullover, sweater, *anything that jumps:* athlete, flea, *etc.*

JUN June

JUNCTION T, *indicates joining letter(s)*

JNR junior

JUNE girl's name, Jun

JUNIOR j(n)r, minor, son

JUSTICE J, JP

K constant, grand, kay, Kelvin, kilo, king, knight, Köchel, potassium, thousand

KAY girl, *indicates the letter* 'k'

KEEP board, stronghold

KELVIN K

KENT SE, garden (of England)

KENTUCKY Ky

KEY A, B, C, D, E, F, G, central, clue, important, major, minor

KG Knight of the Garter

KICK-OFF ko

KILO K

KIN relation, relative, *any example:* ma, pa, sis, *etc.*

KINE cattle, oxen, neat

KING card, chess(man), chess piece, HM, K, R, Rex, ruler, *any example:* George (GR), Lear, *etc.*

KISS x
KITH relation, relative, *any example:* ma, pa, sis, *etc.*
KM kilometre
KNAVE J, Jack, rogue, scamp
KNIGHT chess(man), chess piece, K, KT, sir
KNIGHT OF THE GARTER KG
KNIGHT OF THE THISTLE KT
KNOCK OUT* ko
KNOT speed, *any example:* reef, *etc.*
KNOTTED* tied up
KO kick-off, knockout
KOCHEL K
KT Knight (of the Thistle)
KY Kentucky

L 50, angle, apprentice, beginner, deb, el, ell, fifty, lake, large, Latin, learner, left, length, Liberal, lira, loch, long, lots, lough, many, novice, port, pound, scholar, side, sterling, student, tyro
LA Los Angeles, Louisiana, note, the French
LAB laboratory, Labour, politician, party
LABEL tab, tag
LABORATORY lab
LABOUR childbirth, Lab, left, party, politician, toil, work
LACHESIS Fate
LACK miss, *indicates letter(s) missing*
LACQUER Japan

LAD boy, *any (shortened) name:* Des, Phil, *etc.*
LAH note
LAIR den
LAKE mere, L, loch, lough, tarn, *any example:* Erie, Victoria, *etc.*
LAM beat, hit, pound, strike
LAMBERT Constant
LAMP light
LAND AREA hundred
LANGUAGE tongue, *any example:* Erse, Latin, *etc.*
LARGE big, l, OS
LARGE NUMBER *Any larger Roman numeral:* C, D, L, M
LAST final, stay, *indicates last letter(s)*
LAST MONTH Dec, December, ult
LAST WORD amen
LAT Latin, latitude
LATE d, dead, dec, ex, former, tardy
LATIN L, lat
LATITUDE lat
LAUGH ha(-ha)
LAWMAN DA
LAWRENCE boy, DH, TE
LB extra (leg bye), measure, pound
LE the French
LEAD base metal, go first, guide, Pb, star, van, *indicates first letter(s)*
LEADER captain, chief, *indicates first letter*
LEADING first, *indicates first letter(s)*
LEAF p(age), f(olio)
LEAN thin, list

LEAP jump, spring, vault

LEAR Edward, king, poet

LEARNER apprentice, beginner, L, novice, pupil, student, tyro

LEARNED (= learnéd), BA, MA, Prof, *etc.*

LEE General, river, shelter

LEFT abandoned, gone, Labour, over, port, side, sinister

LEG cricket side, limb, member, on

LEG BYE extra

LENGTH l, *any measurement:* ell, inch, *etc.*

LES Leslie, the French

LESLIE Les

LESS minus, *indicates letter(s) removed*

LET allow(ed), permit(ed), stop

LETTERS* characters, mail, post

LETTUCE cos

LEVEL even, tie

LEW Grade

LIB Liberal, politician, party

LIBERAL free, generous, L, Lib, politician, party

LIBERATED free

LIE rest, story, tale

LIEUTENANT Lt

LIFT jack

LIGHT beam, lamp, not dark, not heavy, ray, Very, window

LIMB arm, leg, member

LIMITED Ltd

LINCOLN (ABRAHAM) Abe

LINE file, railway, rank, row, tier

LINEN Holland

LINES BR, ode, poem, punishment, rly, ry, verse

LINESMAN poet

LING fish, heather

LIONEL Bart

LIQUID *Any example:* ale, beer, *etc.*

LIRA L

LIST cant, heed, index, lean, listen, log, rota, slant, table

LISTEN heed, list

LITTLE *Indicates abbreviation*

LITTLE BY LITTLE *(book title)* Eric, gradually

LITTLE WOMAN Jo

LO look, see

LOAD(S) lots, tons, weight, *indicates large number:* C, D, M, *etc.*

LOCAL inn, PH, pub, tavern

LOCALITY area, quarter, region, *any district:* EC, NE, *etc.*

LOCH L, lake, lough, *any example:* Ness, *etc.*

LOCK forward, tress

LODGER pg, paying guest

LOG book, enter, logarithm, record

LOGARITHM log

LONG l, pine

LONG PLAY LP

LONG TIME age, era, eon

LOOK air, appearance, aspect, bearing, dekko, lo, see, peep, peer, vide

LOOKER eye

LOOT sack, spoils, swag

LOP cut, *indicates letter(s) removed*

LORDS (HOUSE OF) House

LOS ANGELES LA

LOT(S) many, *indicates large number:* C, D, M

LOUD f, ff, forte

LOUGH L, loch, *any example:* Erne, *etc.*

LOUISIANA LA

LOVE adore, amour, cupid, dear, duck, nil, nothing, nought, 0, zero

LOVE AFFAIR amour

LOW blue, cartoonist, down, moo, sad

LOWER cow

LOWDOWN gen

LP disc, long play, record

LSD drug, money

LT Lieutenant

LTD limited

M em, Frenchman, grand, great number, maiden, male, Malta, man, many, mark, married, masculine, mass, master, member, meridiem, metre, midday, mile, Monday, monsieur, motorway, noon, thousand

MA degree, graduate, Massachusetts, Master of Arts, Mother, Mum, scholar

MAC Scot(sman), *indicates Scottish word*

MAD* crazy, wild

MADAME Mme

MADEMOISELLE Mlle

MAG magazine, periodical

MAGAZINE bullets, mag, periodical

MAGISTRATE beak, JP, judge

MAGNESIUM Mg

MAKE* do, construct, manufacture, produce

MAIDEN m, miss, virgin

MAIL letters, post, *sounds like* male

MAIN sea

MAIN FORCE navy, RN

MAINE Me

MAKE fashion, force

MAKE FAST moor

MALE he, m, masculine

MALLARD duck

MALTA M

MAN chap, chess piece, fellow, he, him, IOM, Island, Isle, m, male, Mr, sailor, soldier

MANAGE(S) run(s)

MANAGING DIRECTOR MD

MANGANESE Mn

MANUAL guide

MANUFACTURE* make

MANUSCRIPT ms, mss

MANY lots, *indicates large number:* C, D, M, *etc.*

MAR* March, married, spoil

MARCH Mar

MARCH PAST April

MARINE jolly, RM

MARINER AB, Jack, tar, sailor

MARK boy, m, scar, tick

MARKET E(E)C

MARRIED hitched, m, mar, spliced, wed

MARYLAND MD

MASCULINE butch, m, male

MASS M, Massachusetts, service

MASSACHUSETTS Ma, Mass

MASTER ace, beak, captain, dab, expert, M, MA, painter, teacher, skipper, tutor

MASTER OF ARTS MA

MASTER OF CEREMONIES MC

MATCH contest, fit, test

MATERIAL cloth, fabric, important, *any example:* drill, net, rep, *etc.*

MAYBE* perhaps, say

MAYFAIR West End, WI (= W1)

MB Bachelor of Medicine, doctor

MBE decoration, medal

MC decoration, Master of Ceremonies, medal, Military Cross, Monaco

MD Doctor (of Medicine), Managing Director, Maryland, Musical Director

ME I (object), Maine, Middle East, Middle English, note

MEASURE dance, degree, gauge, tot, *any (abbreviated) example:* centimetre, ell, em, en, foot, inch, kilometre, ounce, perch, pole, rod, yard, *etc.*

MEDAL gong, any example such as MBE, MC

MEDICAL MAN Dr, doc, MB, MO, *etc.*

MELPONE Muse

MEMBER arm, leg, limb, M, MP

MERCURY Hermes, Hg, quicksilver

MERCY quarter

MERIDIEM m, midday, middle, N, noon

MESS* hash

METRE m

MEX Mexico

MEXICO MEX

MG car, magnesium

MI motorway (= M1), note

MIDDAY m, meridiem, n, noon

MIDDLE meridiem

MIDDLE EAST/ENGLISH ME

MILE m

MILITARY CROSS MC, medal

MILITARY MEDAL MM

MILITARY MAN GI, Tommy, Cpl, Lt, Sgt, *etc.*

MILITARY POLICE MP, redcap

MILLIMETRE mm

MINCE* cockney eye, food, meat,

MINE my (poetic), shaft, pit

MING Chinese

MINUS less, *indicates omission of letter(s)*

MISS avoid, girl('s name), maiden, Mississippi

MISSING *Indicates omission of letter(s)*

MISSISSIPPI Miss

MISSOURI Mo

MISTAKE* err, bloomer, sin

MISTER Mr

MISTRESS Mrs

MLLE French girl, Mademoiselle

MM Frenchmen, Military Medal, millimetre, two thousand

MME Madame

MN Manganese

MO doctor, Missouri, moment, second

MOBSTER gangster

MODEL T (Ford)

MOMENT importance, mo, second

MONACO MC

MONDAY M, Mon

MONEY brass, cash, LSD, p, penny, *any example:* cents, dollars, pounds, *etc.*

MONK brother, Dom, Fra, member of order, *any example:* Dominican, *etc.*

MONSIEUR M

MONTH *Any (abbreviated) example:* Jan, Feb Mar, *etc.*

MOO low

MOOR make fast, Othello

MOORING ROPE painter

MORNING am

MOTHER dam, ma, mum, *etc.*

MOTORWAY M, MI (= MI)

MOUNT horse, gee-gee, gg, mountain, *indicates letter(s) on top*

MOUNTAIN(S) mt, mount, range, *any example:* Alps, Ida, *etc.*

MOVE SLOWLY inch

MP Member (of Parliament), Military/Mounted Police, politician, redcap, representative

MPH rate, speed

MR mister

MRS mistress, wife

MRS MOPP char

MS manuscript, (hand)writing

MU Greek character

MUDDLED* confused, fuddled, tangled

MUG face

MUM ma, mother, quiet

MURPHY potato, spud

MUSES Calliope, Clio, Erato, Euterpe, Melpone, Polyhymnia, Terpsichore, Thalia, Urania

MUSEUM BM

MUSIC *Any notes:* A, B, C, Do(h), Re, Me, breve, quaver, *etc.*, *any form:* classical, rock, *etc.*

MUSICAL *Any example:* Evita, Hair, *etc.*

MUSICAL DIRECTOR MD

MUSICAL DIRECTIONS *Any example:* f, ff, forte, p, pp, *etc.*

MUSICAL INSTRUMENT *Any example:* cornet, oboe, piano, *etc.*

MUSICIAN player, *any example:* oboist, pianist, *etc.*

MUSICIANS orchestra, players

MUSKETEERS Aramis, Athos, Porthos

MY gracious, goodness

N bearing, born, bridge player, course, direction, en, meridiem, midday, name, neuter, new, nitrogen, noon, north, Norway, noun, partner (bridge), point, pole, quarter

NA sodium

NAG horse, scold

NAME call, n, reputation, title, *any example:* Dan, Dora, *etc.*

NARCOTIC drug, *any example:* hash, hemp, grass, *etc.*

NARRATIVE account

NAT born, national

NATION race

NATIONAL(ITY) nat, *any example:* Am(erican), Brit(ish), Germ(an), *etc.*

NATIONAL TRUST NT

NATIVITY birth

NAVY colour, fleet, RN, ships, tars

NB nota bene, (take) note

NCO Cpl, non-commissioned officer, RSM, Sergeant, Sgt

ND no date

NE bearing, born, north-east, Tyneside, quarter

NEAT cattle, cow, kine, ox(en)

NEE born

NEGATIVE no

NESS cape, head(land), loch, point

NET capture, catch, ensnare, fabric, material, trap

NETHERLANDS NL

NEUTER n

NEVER-NEVER hire-purchase, HP

NEW* fresh, n, novel

NEW TESTAMENT NT

NEW YORK city, NY

NEW ZEALAND NZ

NEWS gen, info

NEWSPAPER daily, *any example: Express, Times, etc.*

NEWSPAPERMAN ed

NI nickel, Northern Ireland

NIB writer

NICE pleasant, resort

NICK (small) boy, gaol, jail, prison, swipe, take

NICKEL Ni, coin

NIL duck, love, no, nothing, nought, O, zero

NINE IX

NITROGEN N

NL Holland, Netherlands

NO negative, nil, not out, number, 0, refusal, refuse

NOBLEMAN lord, peer, *any example:* don, earl, peer, *etc.*

NO CHARGE free

NO DATE nd

NOISE din, row, uproar, *indicates sounds like*

NOISY f, ff, forte

NOMAD gypsy, wanderer

NOMADIC* wandering

NON (French) refusal

NON-COMMISSIONED OFFICER Corporal, Cpl, NCO

NON-DRINKER abstainer, TT

NOON m, meridiem, midday, n

NOR Norway, or not

NORM average, par, small boy, standard

NORTH bearing, direction, N, point, pole, quarter, sea

NORTH-EAST NE

NORTHERN IRELAND NI

NORTH-WEST NW

NORWAY N, Nor

NOSE beak

NOT refuse

NOTA BENE nb

NOT DARK/HEAVY light

NOT IN out

NOT ON off

NOT OUT at home, batting, in, no

NOT WELL ill

NOTCH score

NOTE nb, notice, *any musical example:* A, B, C, D, E, F, G, Do(h), Re, Me/Mi, Fa(h), So(h), Sol, La(h), Te/Ti; breve, crotchet, minim, semibreve, quaver, *etc., any paper money:* fiver, *etc.*

NOTES currency, music

NOTHING FA, love, nil, nought, 0, zero

NOTICE ad, advertisement, bill, poster, see

NOUGHT duck, love, nil, nothing, 0, zero

NOUN n

NOUS brains

NOWADAYS ad, present

NOVEL new, *any example: Middlemarch, She, etc.*

NOVELIST writer, *any example:* Lear, Poe, *etc.*

NT bible, books, New Testament

NUMBER count, no, tell, *any example:* I, II, III, IV, V, VI, VII, VIII, IX, X, L, C, D, M; ein, one, un(e), *etc.* une, I (= 1)

NUN member of order, sister, *any example:* Cistercian, *etc.*

NUR National Union of Railwaymen

NURSE sister, tend

NUT (National Union of) Teachers

NW bearing, direction, North West, quarter

NY New York

NYM Corporal

NZ New Zealand

O ask, ball, beg, circle, circuit, dial, disc, duck, egg, love, nil, no, nothing, nought, Oh, Ohio, ought, oxygen, plead, ring, request, round, vowel, zero

OAP pensioner, senior citzen

OAR scull

OARSMEN crew, eight, oarsmen, rowers, scullers

OB died, obit, Old Boy

OBE Order of the British Empire

OBEISANCE bow

OBIT ob

OBJECT aim, but, disapprove, end, point, thing

OBOIST airman, musician, player

OBSTACLE bar

OC Officer Commanding

OCCIDENT(AL) W(est/ern)

OCCUPATIONAL THERAPY OT

ODD* bizarre, queer, strange, uneven, *indicates odd letters*

ODE lines, poem

OE Old English

OF THE FRENCH de, de la, des, du

OFF bad, cricket side, not on

OFFENSIVE attack, rank

OFFICER *Any example:* Adm, Brig, Cap, Capt, CO, Col, *etc.*

OFFICER COMMANDING OC

OFFSPRING daughter, issue, son

OH ask, beg, O, Ohio, plead, request

OHIO O, Oh

OHMS On Her Majesty's Service, resistance units

OK all right, good, okay

OKAY all right, good, OK

OLD(EN) aged, ancient, archaic, ex, former, once, *indicates old usage*

OLD BOY OB

OLD CITY Ur

OLD TESTAMENT OT

OLD ENGLISH OE

OLD MONEY bob, d, p(enny), s(hilling), *any example:* groat, *etc.*

OM Order of Merit

ON* about, concerning, cricket side, leg, playing, *indicates letter(s) above/below*

ON BOARD *Indicates letters between* 'SS'

ON HORSEBACK up

ONCE archaic, ex, former, old, one-time

ONE a, ace, an, I (= 1)

ONE COMING OUT deb, debutante

ONE HUNDRED century

ONE-TIME archaic, ex, former, once, old

OP operation, opus, out of print, work

OPERATION op

OPPOSITE *Indicates antonym*

OPUS Op, work

OR alternatively, gold

OR NOT nor

ORCHESTRA musicians, players

ORDER* adjust, arrange, class, command, decoration, instruct, holy order, *any example of honour:* OBE, OM, *etc.*

ORDER OF THE BRITISH EMPIRE OBE

ORDER OF MERIT OM

ORDINARY SEAMAN OS

ORGAN *Any example:* ear, *etc.*

ORGANIZATION* *Any example:* AA, RAC, UN, *etc.*

ORIENT China, E, Japan

ORIENT(AL) Chinese, E(ast/ern), Japanese

ORNAMENT decoration

OS AB, big, extra large, outsize, Ordinary Seaman, sailor, tar, very big

OT bible, books, Old Testament, occupational therapy

OTHELLO Moor

OTHERS rest

OUGHT O

OUNCE cat, measure, oz

OUSE river

OUT* blooming, not in, *any dismissal in cricket:* b(owled), c(aught), st(umped), *etc.*

OUT OF ex, from

OUT OF PRINT op

OUTSIZE big, extra, huge, large, OS

OVA eggs

OVER above, concerning, dead, done, ended, in charge (of), left, re, six balls/deliveries, *indicates letter(s) above*

OVERTURN(ED)* upset, *indicates letters reading backwards in Down clue*

OVUM egg

OWE(S) IOU(s)

OWN have

OWNER proprietor

OX bull, neat

OXEN cattle, kine, neat

OXFORD shoe, university

OXYGEN O

OZ Australia, ounce, wizard place

P copper, money, page, Panama, parking, pawn, penny, phosphorus, piano, port, Portugal, power, president, soft(ly), quiet

PA dad, father, Panama, Pennsylvania, Philadelphia, pop, sire

PACK cards, hunt

PAGE(S) p, pp

PAINTER artist, master, mooring rope, RA, *any example:* Tiepolo, Titian, *etc.*

PAINTING at

PAIR pr, *indicates doubling of letter/word*

PALE ashen, fence, wan

PANAMA Pa

PAPERBACK pb

PAPERS press

PAR average, norm, standard

PARENTAL GUIDANCE PG

PARISIAN *Indicates French word*

PARKING P

PARLIAMENT House

PARLIAMENTARY PRIVATE SECRETARY PPS

PART bit, role, piece, *indicates hidden word or part of word*

PARTNER N, S, E, W (bridge)

PARTY do, fete, *any example:* Con(servative, Lab(our), Lib(eral), Tory, *etc.*

PAS dance, fathers, step

PASS col, hand

PATE head, starter

PAWN chess piece, man, P, pledge, pop

PAWNBROKER uncle

PAY fee, salary, wage

PAYING GUEST lodger, PG

PB lead, paperback

PC bobby, copper, police constable, policeman, postcard

PE Peru, physical education, PT

PECKER beak

PED pedestrian

PEDESTRIAN dull, ped, walker

PEELER copper, PC, policeman

PEG (little) Margaret, tee

PEN author, enclosure, prison, swan, write(r)

PENCIL writer, *any type:* B, BB, HB, *etc.*

PENNY coin, copper, d, girl's name, money, p

PENNSYLVANIA Pa

PENSIONER OAP, senior citizen

PER a, by, ea, (for) each

PERCH fish, measure, pole, rod, roost

PERFORM act, do

PERHAPS* maybe, say

PERI fairy

PERIOD AD, age, BC, eon, era, stop, *any example:* hour, min, *etc.*

PERIODICAL mag, magazine

PERMIT allow, grant, let

PERSONAL private

PERSONALITY character, ego, id

PERU PE

PET favourite

PETER boy, dynamite, fisherman, man, safe

PHILADELPHIA Pa

PHILOSOPHER *Any example:* Mill, Plato, *etc.*

PG lodger, parental guidance, paying guest

PH inn, pub, tavern

PHIL small boy, man, Philadelphia, Philharmonic, philosophy

PHILADELPHIA Pa, Phil

PHILANTHROPIST Tate

PHILHARMONIC Phil

PHILOSOPHY phil

PHONE call, dial, ring, telephone

PHOSPHORUS P

PHYSICAL EXERCISE PE, PT

PHYSICAL TRAINING PE, PT

PI devout, Greek letter, pious, religious

PIANISSIMO pp, very soft(ly)

PIANIST musician

PIANO grand, musical instrument, p, soft(ly)

PICK elite, flower

PIECE man, *any chess piece:* pawn, rook, *etc.*

PINE long, tree

PIOUS devout, pi, religious

PISTOL gat, gun

PIT hell, mine, shaft

PLA Port (of London) Authority

PLANET heavenly body, *any example:* Mars, *etc.*

PLANT factory, *any example:* climber, daff, pink, *etc.*

PLATES china, cockney feet

PLAY act(s), drama, scenes

PLAYER actor, musician, record, thespian

PLAYERS cast, musicians, orchestra, records, side, team, XI, XV

PLAYING* in, on

PLAY VIOLIN bow, fiddle

PLEAD beg, O, Oh

PLEASANT nice

PLEDGE pawn, pop, token

PLO terrorists

PLOUGH fail, work on farm

PLUMB sound, *sounds like fruit*

PLUTO Dis, dog, Erebus, Hades, heavenly body, Hell, planet, Underworld

PLUTONIUM Pu

PM afternoon, post meridiem, post mortem, Prime Minister

PO Pilot Officer, Post Office, postal order, river

POEM lines, ode

POET linesman, *indicates poetic form of word, any example:* anon, Keats, Shelley, *etc.*

POETIC(ALLY) *Indicates poetic form of word*

POINT N(orth), S(outh), E(ast) W(est), dot, cape, fielder, head, ness, object, stop, tip

POINT OF VIEW angle

POINTS score, try

POLE N(orth), S(outh), East European, measure, perch, rod

POLICE bobbies, CID, coppers, force,

POLICE CONSTABLE PC

POLICEMAN bobby, copper, MP, PC, peeler

POLITICIAN Con(servative), Lab(our), Lib(eral), MP, Republican, Tory

POLYHYMNIA Muse

POOR ACTOR ham

POP dad, father, pa, pawn, pledge, popular, sire

PORT bearing, carriage, gateway, harbour, L, left, P, Portugal, wine, *any example:* Dover, Rio, *etc.*

PORT AUTHORITY PLA

PORTHOS Musketeer

PORTUGAL P, Port

POSSIBLY* maybe, perhaps

POST job, letters, mail

POST MERIDIEM pm

POST MORTEM PM

POST OFFICE GPO, PO

POSTAL ORDER PO

POSTCARD pc

POSTER ad, advertisement, bill, notice

POSTSCRIPT afterthought, PPS, PS, *indicates letter(s) added*

POTASSIUM K

POTATO murphy, spud

POUND enclosure, l, lb

POW prisoner (of war)

POWER P, *any measurement:* amp, volt, watt, *etc.*

PP pianissimo, tuppence, very soft

PPS afterthought, parliamentary private secretary, postscript, *indicates letter(s) added*

PR price, public relations

PRACTICE custom, usage, use

PRE(-) ante, before

PRES president

PRESENT (TIME) AD, now, Christmas

PRESERVE Can

PRESIDENT P, Pres

PRESS iron, papers, urge

PRICE pr

PRIEST father, fr, priest, pr, Rev, *any example:* Eli, *etc.*

PRIESTS clergy, cloth

PRIME MINISTER PM

PRINCE(SS) HRH, P, Pr, *any example:* Di, Diana, Margaret, *etc.*

PRINCIPAL capital

PRINTER'S MEASURE em, en

PRISON gaol, jail, jug, pen, stir, *any example:* Fleet, Reading, *etc.*

PRISON SENTENCE stretch, time

PRISONER POW, *indicates letter(s) inside*

PRIVATE GI, personal, Pte, soldier, Tommy

PRO ace, expert, for, Public Relations Officer

PRODUCE* construct, make

PROF Professor

PROFESSIONAL ace, dab, expert, pro

PROFESSOR Prof

PRONOUN *Any example:* I, me, my, he, his, her, *etc.*

PROP forward, proprietor, support

PROP UP support, *indicates letters supported in Down clue*

PROPHET seer, *any example:* Amos, Isaiah, *etc.*

PROPRIETOR owner, prop

PS afterthought, postscript, *indicates letter(s) added*

PT PE, (physical) exercise, (physical) training

PUB(LIC HOUSE) inn, local, PH, tavern

PUBLIC RELATIONS (OFFICER) PR(O)

PUBLISH issue

PUMP question, shoe
PUNISHMENT lines
PUPIL iris, L, learner, scholar, student
PUT set
PUT IN *Indicates letter(s) inserted*
PUT ON don

Q Quebec, queen, question
QC Queen's Counsel, silk
QT quart, quiet
QU quart, queen
QUA whereby (Latin)
QUALITY grade
QUART qt, qu
QUARTER area, coin, mercy, *any example:* N, S, E, W, NE, SW, *etc.*
QUARTET four
QUEBEC Q
QUEEN card, chess piece, ER, HM, Q, Qu, R, Regina, ruler, *any example:* Anne, Victoria, *etc.*
QUEEN'S COUNSEL QC, silk
QUESTION grill, pump, q
QUEUE rank
QUEER* odd, strange
QUICK fast, fleet
QUICKSILVER Mercury
QUIET(LY) hush, p, pp, qt, sh

R castle, king, queen, radius, recipe, regina, repeat, resistance, rex, right, river, road, Romania, rook, royal, run(s), side, starboard, take

RA artillery, artist, Burlington House, god, gunners, painter, radium, Royal Academy, Royal Artillery
RAB Butler
RAC Royal Armoured Corps, Royal Automobile Club
RACE nation, run, TT
RADICAL root
RADIUM Ra
RADIUS r
RAF airmen, Royal Air Force
RAGE* anger, ire
RAGGED* untidy
RAILWAY BR, line, rly, ry, *any example:* GWR, LMS, LNER, SR, *etc.*
RAILMEN NUR
RAISE rear, *indicates letters reversed in Down clue*
RAM Aries, butter, sheep, tup
RAMBLING* roaming, wandering
RANDOM* haphazard
RANGE mountains, *any example:* Andes, Alps, Urals, *etc.*
RANK class, foul, grade, offensive, queue, tier
RANSACKED* wrecked
RASCAL imp, rogue, scamp
RAT deserter, scab
RATE assess, knot, mph, speed
RATING AB, Jack, sailor, tar, tax
RAY beam, fish, shaft
RC Church, Red Cross, Roman Catholic
RD road, Rural Dean
RE about, again, concerning, note, over, Religious Education,

Royal Engineers Sapper(s), Soldier(s)

REAR raise, stern

REBEL* revolt, revolutionary, *any example:* Cade, Straw, Tyler, *etc.*

RECEIVER fence

RECIPE* r, take

RECORD disc, enter, entry, EP, log, LP, player

RED bloody, communist, revolutionary, Russian

REDCAP bird, Military Policeman, MP

RED CROSS RC

REFUSAL no

REFUSE no, non, not, rot, rubbish, tripe

REGINA Q(ueen), R

RELATION bearing, kith, kin, tale, *any example:* aunt, bro, dad, *etc.*

RELATIVE kith, kin, *any example:* ma, pa, sis, *etc.*

RELIGIOUS devout, holy, pi, pious

RELIGIOUS EDUCATION RE

RELIGIOUS INSTRUCTION RI

RELIGIOUS PERSON DD, Rev(d), *etc.*

REMIND jog

REORGANIZED* altered, changed

REORDERED* changed, reshaped, scrambled

REP agent, material, MP, repertory, representative, republican, salesman, traveller

REPEAT r, *indicates repetition of letter(s)*

REPERTORY rep

REPLACED* changed

REPLY ans, answer

REPTILE *Any example:* adder, *etc.*

REPRESENTATIVE agent, MP, rep, salesman, traveller

REPUBLICAN politician, rep

REPUTATION name

REQUEST ask, beg, o, oh

RES (Latin) thing

RESERVE book, ice

RESHAPED* reordered

RESISTANCE ohm, R

RESORT* spa, *any example:* Bath, Nice, *etc.*

REST bridge, lie, others

RESTING asleep, RIP, *indicates letter(s) in* 'bed' *or* 'cot'

RET soak

RETIRE(D) *Indicates letters reversed; indicates letters in* 'bed' *or* 'cot'

RETREAT den, *indicates letters reversed*

REV(D) vicar

REVOLT* rebel, revolution

REVOLTING* rebelling

REVOLUTION* revolt

REVOLUTIONARY* agitator, Che, rebel, red, wheel

REX boy, Harrison, king, R

RFC Rugby (Football Club), Royal Flying Corps

RHODE ISLAND RI

RI Rhode Island, Religious Instruction

RID free

RIGHT correct, dexter, r, rt, side, starboard, Tories, Tory

RIGHT REVEREND RR, Bishop

RILL brook, flower, runner, stream

RING call, circle, circuit, dial, O, phone, telephone

RIP* rest in peace, tear

RIVER flower, R, runner, *any example:* Dee, Exe, Po, *etc.*

RIVULET brook, flower, runner, stream

RLY lines, railway

RM jolly, (Royal) Marine

RN fleet, force, Royal Navy

ROAD rd, st, street, way

ROAMING* rambling, wandering

ROCK gem, music, stone, *any example:* granite,

ROD pole, perch, staff

ROGUE imp, rascal scamp

ROLLS-ROYCE RR

ROM roman

ROMAN Rom, *indicates Latin word*

ROMAN CATHOLIC RC

ROMANIA R

ROOK bird, castle, cheat, chess piece, do, R

ROOST perch

ROT corruption, rubbish, tripe

ROUND circle, O, ring, *indicates letter(s) around/within word*

ROUTE direction, road

ROW* din, line, noise, oar, scull, tier, uproar

ROWERS crew, eight, oarsmen

ROYAL colour (blue), paper size, R

ROYAL ACADEMY Burlington House, RA

ROYAL AIR FORCE airmen, RAF

ROYAL ARMOURED CORPS RAC

ROYAL ARTILLERY arsenal, gunners, RA

ROYAL AUTOMOBILE CLUB RAC

ROYAL ENGINEER(S) RE, sapper(s)

ROYAL MARINE(S) jolly, RM

ROYAL NAVY fleet, force, RN

RR bishop, Right Reverend, Rolls-Royce

RSM NCO, Regimental Sergeant Major

RT right

RU Rugby Union

RUBBISH* rot, tripe

RUGBY (UNION) RFC, RU

RUIN* spoil

RULER emperor, king, queen, tsar, *any example:* Ivan, Victoria, *etc.*

RUN(S) manage(s), r, race(s)

RUNNER flower, R, river

RUNNER UP second

RURAL DEAN RD

RUSSIA USSR *(less common now)*

RUSSIAN Ivan, red,

RV bible, revised version

RY lines, railway

S bearing, bend, bob, bridge player, course, direction, dollar, holy man, es(s), partner, pole, quarter, Sabbath, saint, Saturday, second, shilling, small, son, South(ern), sulphur, sun, Sunday, Sweden

SA It, sex appeal, South Africa, South America, (the) thing

SABBATH S

SABLE black
SACK fire, loot, sherry
SAD blue, down, low
SAFE peter
SAILOR AB, Jack, man, OS, rating, salt, tar
SAINT good man, holy man, S, St
SAINTS SS
SALESMAN rep, representative, traveller
SALT sailor, season
SAME ditto, do
SAP ass, dolt, fool, undermine
SAPPER(S) engineer(s), RE, Royal Engineer(s)
SAS Special Air Service
SAT Saturday
SATURDAY S, Sat
SAUCE HP
SAUCER UFO
SAUSAGE banger
SAY eg, for example, for instance, maybe, perhaps, state
SCAMP imp, rascal, rogue
SCAN con, read
SCAR mark
SCATTER* throw out
SCHOLAR BA, L, MA, pupil, student
SCOLD nag
SCHOOL sch, fish(es), swimmers, *any example*: Eton, Harrow, *etc.*
SCIENCE sc
SCIENTIST BSc, *any example:* Bacon, Darwin, *etc.*
SCORE notch, twenty, XX, *any example:* goal, try, *etc.*
SCOT tax, *any name of Scotsman:* Ian, Jock, Mac, *etc.*

SCOTSMAN mon, *any name of Scotsman:* Bruce, Sandy, *etc.*
SCOTTISH *Indicates Scottish word, pronunciation*
SCRAMBLED* reordered
SCULL oar, row
SE bearing, direction, Home Counties, Kent, quarter, Selenium, south-east
SEA deep, main, *any example:* Dead, North, *etc.*
SEASON autumn, spring, summer, winter, salt, time, tide
SEC dry, second, secretary
SECOND b (second class, letter, *etc.*), back, mo, moment, runner-up, s, sec, tic
SECOND-HAND sh
SECOND THOUGHTS ps, pps
SECRET POLICE SS
SECRETARY sec
SECTION chapter, *indicates hidden word*
SEE bishopric, lo, look, notice, peer, v, vide, *any example:* Ely, Rome, *etc.*
SELF ego, id
SENIOR major, snr
SENIOR CITIZEN OAP
SENOR Spaniard, Spanish man, Sr
SEPTEMBER Sep, Sept
SERGE cloth, Sergeant
SERGEANT NCO, Sgt
SERIOUS grave, stern
SERPENT (musical) instrument, *any example:* asp, python, *etc.*
SERVICE ace, china, mass, tree, *any example:* army, airforce, navy, RAF, RN, *etc.*

SET cluster, group, put
SEX APPEAL It, SA, (the) thing
SGT NCO, Sergeant
SH hush, quiet, Shetlands
SHADE hue, colour, ghost, shadow
SHAFT mine, ray
SHAKESPEARE Bard
SHE female, *(title of)* novel, woman
SHEEP ewe, ram, teg, tup
SHELTER lee
SHERRY sack
SHETLANDS Sh
SHILLING bob, s
SHIP boat, SS, vessel, *any example:* brig, cruiser, ketch, liner, sloop, *etc.*
SHIPS fleet, navy
SHIVER brr
SHORT *Indicates shortened form*
SHORTLY anon, soon, *indicates shortened form*
SHOE Oxford, pump, *etc.*
SHOP grass, inform, sing
SHOUT call
SHOW display, *any example: Evita, Hair, etc.*
SIB brother, sibling, sister
SIBLING brother, sib, sister
SICK* ill
SIDE eleven, fifteen, l(eft), players, r(ight), team, XI, XV
SILK QC, Queen's Counsel
SILVER Ag
SIMPLETON ass, dope, dolt, fool, sap
SIN err, evil, wrong, *any example*: gluttony, sloth, *etc.*
SING grass, inform
SINGER informer, *any example:*

alto, baritone, bass, tenor, soprano, *etc.*
SINGLE I (= 1), unmarried
SINISTER left
SIR knight
SIRE dad, father, pa, pop
SIR PETER Brook
SIS sister
SISTER nun, nurse, sib, sibling, sis
SIX boundary, VI
SIXTH FORM upper class
SKILL art
SKIPPER Capt, captain, master
SLANT angle, lean, list
SLEEP doze, kip, nap, nod, zz
SLEIGH bob
SLOTH* ai, idleness, sin
SMALL s, *indicates diminuitive, shortened version, particularly names, states*
SMASH* break, hit, shot,
SMUG pi
SNAGGED caught, trapped, *indicates (anagram) letter(s) within a word*
SNAKE *Any example:* adder, viper, *etc.*
SNARED* caught, trapped
SNORING zz
SO ergo, note, such, therefore, thus
SOAK ret
SOCIAL WORKER ant
SOCIALLY ACCEPTABLE U, OK
SOCIETY soc
SODIUM Na
SOFT(LY) p, piano, pp, sh
SO(H) note

SOL sun, note
SOLDIER man, Private, Tommy, RE, *any example:* Col, Gen, *etc.*
SOLDIERS army, company, men, REs, TA, *etc.*
SOME part, *indicates hidden word, part of word*
SOME FRENCH de, de la, des, du
SOME WAY* somehow
SOMEHOW* some way
SOMERSAULT *Indicates letters/ word reversal*
SON boy, offspring, s, issue
SOON anon
SOUND fit, plumb, *indicates sounds like*
SOUP* course
SORT* type
SOUTH bearing, direction, point, pole, quarter, S
SOUTH AFRICA(N) Boer, SA
SOUTH EAST SE
SOUTH WEST SW
SP betting, odds, starting price
SPA resort, spring
SPAIN E
SPANIARD Don, Senor, Sr
SPANISH *Indicates Spanish word*
SPANNER arch, bridge, tool
SPASM* fit, tic, turn
SPEAK orate, *indicates sounds like*
SPECIAL AIR SERVICE SAS
SPEED knot, mph, rate
SPIES agents, CIA, intelligence, MIV (= MI5), sees
SPILL* overturn, upset
SPIRIT ghost, shade, *any example:* gin, rum, vodka, *etc.*
SPLICED married, wed

SPLIT* *Indicates letter(s) introduced to word*
SPOIL(S)* loot, mar(s), swag
SPOON stirrer
SPRING leap, jump, season, spa
SPUD murphy
SPUR egg
SQUARE T
SR Senor, Spaniard
SS boat, dollars, Gestapo, saints, Secret Police, (steam)ship, steamer, vessel
ST good man, holy man, saint, stone, street, road
STAFF hands, rod, workers
STANDARD average, degree, flag, norm, par
STAR heavenly body, lead, *any example:* Sirius, sun, *etc.*
STARBOARD r, right, rt
STARTING PRICE SP
STARTER beginner, course, deb, learner, L, novice, tyro
STATE aver, say, *any example, particularly abbreviated US:* Ala, Cal, Ga, Mass, *etc.*
STEAL move quietly, nick, take
STEAMER cruiser, liner, ship, ss
STEP pas
STERLING L
STERN back, rear, serious
STEW* cook
STIR* agitate, gaol, jail, mix
STIRRER agitator, spoon
STOLEN hot
STONE gem, flag, st, *any example:* diamond, granite, ruby, *etc.*
STOP cease, halt, point
STOP UP dam

STORY account, lie, tale
STRANGE* bizarre, odd, queer, unknown
STRAY* err, wander, wanderer
STREAM brook, flower, rill, runner
STRETCH expand, sentence, time (in prison),
STREET road, rd, st, way
STRICKEN hit, ill
STRIKE hit, lam, rap, tap
STRONG f, ff
STRONGHOLD castle, fort
STUD boss
STUDENT L, learner, pupil, scholar
STUDY con, den, read, scan
STY filthy place
STYE eyesore
SUB submarine, U-boat, under
SUBMARINE sub, U-boat
SUBMIT bow, undergo
SUBURB *Any example:* Sheen, Tooting, *etc.*
SUCH so
SULPHUR S
SUMMER adder, BST, season
SUN S, sol, Sunday
SUNBATHE tan
SUNDAY S, Sun
SUPPORT(ER) bra, easel, prop, second(er), *indicates letter(s) below in Down clue*
SW bearing, direction, quarter, south-west
SWALLOW bird, down, *indicates letter(s) enclosed*
SWAN cob, pen
SWE Sweden
SWEDEN S, Swe

SWIMMER fish, *any example of creature that swims:* eel, otter, *etc.*
SWINDLE cheat, con, do, rook
SWITZERLAND CH

T car, Ford, junction, model, square, tee, time, ton, Tuesday
TA (Territorial) Army, thanks
TABLE board, list
TAFF Welshman
TAIL dog, *indicates last letter(s) of word*
TAKE r, recipe, steal, *indicates letter(s) joined on to word*
TAKE IN trick, *indicates letter(s) enclosed by word*
TAKE ON *Indicates letter(s) joined on to word*
TAKE UP *Indicates letter(s) introduced backwards into word*
TALE account, lie, story
TAN beat, brown, sunbathe
TANGLED* muddled
TAR AB, Jack, OS, rating, sailor, salt
TARDY late
TARN lake, mere
TARS navy
TASTE test, try
TATE gallery, philanthropist
TAVERN inn, local, PH, pub
TAX assess(ment), rating, scot, test, try, VAT
TAXI cab, transport
TE Lawrence, note
TEA cha, char, cuppa

TEACH instruct
TEACHER beak, master
TEACHERS NUT
TEAM eleven, II (= 11), fifteen, XI, XV, players, side, *any example:* Arsenal, Villa, *etc.*
TEAR* drop, rip
TED (small) boy, Dexter, Heath
TEE peg, *indicates the letter* 't'
TEETOTAL AA, abstainer, TT
TEG sheep
TELEPHONE call, dial, phone, ring
TELL archer, bowman, count, number, relate
TEN IO (= 10), X
TEND aid, help, incline, lean, nurse,
TENT camp, canvas
TERPSICHORE Muse
TERRITORIAL ARMY TA
TERRORISTS IRA, PLO
TEST exercise, match, river, tax, try
TESTAMENT NT, OT, will
TH Thursday
THALIA Muse
THAMES Isis, (London) flower, runner
THANKS ta
THAT IS ie
THE (definite) article
THE FRENCH le, la, les
THE GERMAN das, der, die
THE ITALIAN il *(usually)*
THE OLD ye
THE SPANISH el *(usually)*
THEE you (old)
THEM em
THEOLOGIAN DD

THEORY ism
THEREFORE ergo, so
THERMAL UNIT BTU
THESPIAN actor, player
THIN lean
THINE your (old)
THING object, res (Latin), it
THIS MONTH inst
THOU you (old)
THOUGH but, yet
THOUSAND grand, K, M
THREESOME trio
THROUGH by, per, via
THROW* cast, toss
THROW OUT* scatter
THURSDAY Th, Thurs
THUS so
THY your (old)
TI note, titanium, tree
TIC movement, spasm, twitch
TICK credit, mark
TIER line, rank, row
TIME AD, age, am, BC, era, pm, season, t, tide, *any example:* hour, min(ute), sec(ond), *etc.*
TIMES daily
TIN can, cash
TINY wee, *indicates shortened form, particularly names, states*
TIP advice, point
TISIPHONE Fury
TITANIUM Ti
TITLE call, name, *any peer:* lord, lady, *etc.*
TO *Often indicates joined to*
TO AND FRO *Indicates a palindrome*
TO-DO bother, fuss
TOIL labour, work

TOLERATE bear, brook

TOM bell, cat

TOME book, vol, volume

TOMMY Private, soldier

TON C, century, fashion, hundred, t

TONGUE language, *any example:* French, German, *etc.*

TOOL *Any example:* axe, spanner, wrench, *etc.*

TOP ace, cap, first, lid, *indicates first letter(s)*

TORT wrong

TORY C, Con(servative), party, politician, right

TOSS* cast, throw

TOT child, drink, measure

TO THE FRENCH a la, au, aux

TOWN *Any example:* Diss, Rye, York, *etc.*

TNT explosive

TR translator

TRADES UNION CONGRESS TUC, workers

TRAIN coach, instruct, transport

TRAINER coach

TRAINING PE, PT, *etc.*

TRAINS BR, coaches, ry

TRANSLATOR tr

TRANSPORT enchant, entrance, *any example:* BA, BR, bus, cab, car, ry, taxi, train, van, *etc.*

TRAP capture, catch, carriage, ensnare, gin, net, snare, *indicates letter(s) caught within word*

TRAPPED caught, netted, *indicates letter(s) caught within word*

TRAVELLER rep, representative

TREE actor, *any example:* bo, oak, *etc.*

TRESS lock

TRICK con, take in

TRIAL exam, test

TRIER city, judge

TRIO three(some)

TRIPE rot, rubbish

TROT jog

TRY attempt, essay, score, taste, test, three points

TT AA, abstainer, dry, race, teetotal

TUC Trades Union Congress, workers

TUESDAY T, Tues

TUP ram, sheep

TUPPENCE dd, pp

TUNE air

TURN* act, angle, corner, go, spasm, twist, U, *indicates letters reversed*

TUTOR master

TWELVE dozen, XII

TWENTY score, XX

TWICE *Indicates letter(s) repeated*

TWIST* dance, turn

TWITCH tic

TWO company

TWO HUNDRED CC

TWO THOUSAND MM

TYNESIDE NE

TYPE* character, sort

TYRO apprentice, beginner, L, learner, novice, starter

U bend, boat, class, done, fashionable, OK, okay, (socially) acceptable, turn, universal,

university, upper class,
uranium, Uruguay, Utah, vowel
U-BOAT sub, submarine
UFO saucer
UK (Great) Britain, United Kingdom
ULT final, last month, ultimate
ULTIMATE final, ult
UM hesitation
UN a French, international
organization, United Nations
UNCANNY* weird
UNCLE Bob, pawnbroker, relative,
Sam
UNCLE SAM USA
UNDER below, sub, *indicates*
letter(s) below
UNDER SECRETARY US
UNDERGO submit, *indicates*
letter(s) placed below
UNDERMINE sap
UNDERWORLD Dis, Erebus,
gangland, Hades, Hell, Inferno, pit,
Pluto
UNE a French
UNEVEN* odd
UNION *Any example:* NUR, *etc.*
UNITED KINGDOM UK
UNITED NATIONS UN
UNITED STATES (OF
AMERICA) US(A)
UNIVERSAL general, U
UNIVERSITY U
UNKNOWN anon, strange, x, y
UNRAVELLED* untwisted
UNTIDY* ragged
UNTWISTED* unravelled
UP at university, excited, in court,
on horseback, *indicates letter(s)*
reading upwards

UP AGAINST *Indicates (reversed)*
letter(s) adjoining
UPPER CASE capital
UPPER CLASS sixth form, U
UPROAR* row
UPSET* overturn, spill, *indicates*
letters reversed
UR old city
URANIA Muse
URANIUM U
URGE egg, press
URN vessel
URUGUAY U
US Under Secretary, (United) States
(of America), useless, we (object)
USA Uncle Sam, (United) States of
(America)
USAGE custom, practice, use
USE application, custom, practice
USELESS US
UTAH U

V against, five, see, vanadium,
Vatican (City), vee, verse, versus,
velocity, very, vide, victory,
Virginia, volt, vol(ume), vs
VALEDICTION bye
VAN front, vehicle
VANADIUM V
VARIATION* change
VARNISH Japan
VAT container, tax
VATICAN (CITY) V
VAULT jump, leap, safe, spring
VEE *Indicates letter* 'v'
VELOCITY v

VERMOUTH It, Italian
VERSE lines, ode, poetry, v
VERSUS against, v, vs
VERY light, v
VERY BIG OS
VERY IMPORTANT PERSON VIP
VERY LOUD(LY)/NOIS(IL)Y ff, fortissimo
VERY SOFT(LY) pp, pianissimo
VESSEL boat, bowl, can, ship, SS, urn, *any example:* brig, ketch, liner, *etc.*
VET doctor, veteran, veterinary surgeon
VETERAN vet
VETERINARY SURGEON vet
VI bomb (= V1), (little) girl, six, Violet
VIA by, per, through
VICAR Rev(d)
VICTORIA lake, ruler, VR
VICTORY V
VIDE lo, look, see, V
VIOLET (little) girl, flower, Vi
VIOLINIST bowman, fiddler, player
VIP celebrity, very important person
VIRGIN maiden
VIRGINIA Va
VOL book, cc, tome, v, volume
VOLKSWAGEN Beetle
VOLT v
VOLUME book, cc, tome, v, vol
VOTE x
VOWEL a, e, i, o, u
VS against, V, versus

W bearing, bridge player, course, direction, extra (cricket), occident(al), point, quarter, watt, Wednesday, West(ern), wicket, wide, width, wife, women
WAGER bet, gamble, stake
WALL boundary
WAN ashen, pale
WANDER* err, roam, ramble, stray
WANDERER gypsy, nomad, stray
WANDERING* roaming, rambling
WATER Aq, element
WATT W
WAY av(enue), direction, manner, path, rd, road, route, st(reet),
WE you and I
WEAPON *Any example:* bomb, gun, sword, *etc.*
WEAPONS artillery, guns, *etc.*
WED hitched, married, spliced, we would, Wednesday
WEDNESDAY W, Wed
WEE small, tiny (Scottish), *indicates shortened or diminutive form*
WEEP cry, greet
WEIGHT gravity, importance, measure, *any example:* dram, gram, lb, ounce, oz, pound, *etc.*
WEIRD* uncanny
WELSH *Indicates Welsh name, county, river, town:* Owen, Glam(organ), Usk, Swansea, *etc.*

WELSHMAN Dai, Evans, Jones, Lewis, Taff, *etc.*

WEST bearing, direction, Occident, point, quarter, W

WEST END Mayfair, WI (= WI)

WESTERN Occidental

WEST INDIES WI

WE WOULD wed (= we'd)

WHEEL revolutionary

WHEREBY qua (Latin), *indicates letters adjoining*

WHY *Sounds like* 'y'

WI Mayfair (W1), West End (W1), West Indies, Women's Institute

WICKED* bad, evil

WICKET gate, w

WIDE broad, extra, w(ide)

WIDTH w

WIFE Dutch, Mrs, w

WILD* mad

WILL Bill, testament, William

WILLIAM Bill, Will, Wm

WIND* blower

WINDOW light

WING l(eft), r(ight)

WINGER bird, footballer

WINE colour, drink, vin, vino, *any example:* Claret, Graves, Hock, *etc.*

WINNER first

WITH *Indicates letter(s) adjoining*

WITH ITALIAN con

WITHIN inside, *indicates letter(s) inside*

WIZARD PLACE Oz

WOMAN she, her, lass, madam, miss, Mrs, Ms, *any name:* Ada, Eve, *etc.*

WOMEN w

WOMEN' INSTITUTE WI

WORK* go, labour, op, opus, toil

WORKER ant, bee, hand, man

WORKERS hands, men, staff, TUC, Trades Union Congress

WORRY* harry

WRITE pen

WRITER author, composer, pen, nib, pencil, quill, *any example:* Bacon, Bronte, Chaucer, *etc.*

WRITING ms, mss

WRONG* err, error, crime sin, tort, X

X chromosome, cross, ex, kiss, ten, unknown, vote, wrong

XE Xenon

XI eleven, players, (cricket) side, (football) team

XII dozen, twelve

XL forty

XV fifteen, players, side, (rugby football) team

XX score, twenty

XXX thirty

Y chromosome, unknown, yard, year, yen, young, yttrium, Yugoslavia

YARD CID, detectives, measure, y, yard

YE the (old), you (old)
YEAR y, yr
YEN currency, desire, Y
YET but, though
YOU AND I we, us
YOU OLD thou, thee
YOUNG y, *indicates shortened, diminutive form*
YOU OLD ye
YOUR yr
YOUR OLD thine, thy
YR year, your
YTTRIUM Y
YU Yugoslavia
YUGOSLAVIA Y, YU

Z Zambia, Zanzibar, zed, zero
ZAIRE ZR
ZAMBIA Z
ZANZIBAR Z
ZED *Indicates letter 'z'*
ZERO duck, love, nil, nothing, nought, O (= 0), z
ZINC ZN
ZIRCONIUM ZR
ZN zinc
ZR zirconium, Zaire
ZZ asleep, snoring

Roman Numerals

I one
II two
IV four
V five
VI six
IX nine
X ten
XI eleven
XV fifteen
XVI sixteen

L fifty
LI fifty-one
C one hundred
CL one hundred-and-fifty
CC two hundred
D five hundred
DI five hundred-and-one
M one thousand
MD fifteen hundred
MM two thousand

Help

This section is designed to act as a buffer zone between the puzzles and solutions. It can be used for reference both when you are stuck on a particular clue or when you have got a solution but don't understand how it is constructed or why it is correct.

Various conventions detailed below have been followed when explicating the clue devices.

Roman type indicates words that are directly quoted from clues.
UPPER CASE letters are employed for elements of the solutions.
Italicized type is used to give a plain English paraphrase of the instructional elements within a clue.
'Single quotes' appear around words or phrases that are a prerequisite to a final solution but not the solution itself.

Clue types [a] and [b] are glossed by *Double definition* and *Single definition* respectively because it is rarely easy to explain such clues without giving the solution – which we have tried to avoid doing here. In certain cases, however, we have included an explanation within square brackets of any clues that depend on a rather athletic leap of the imagination.

PUZZLE 1

Across

4 Second = S + coach = trainer **8** *Double definition* **9** cut down =
REAP + fruit = PEAR **10** Period of time = AGE *after* brief = SHORT
11 *Double definition* **12** *Anagram:* machine + first call = C
13 *Single definition* **16** DOWN *following* demonstration = SHOW
19 *Single definition* **21** *Double definition* **23** *Single definition* [Simple
reference to **1** *Dn*] **24** *Anagram:* nice oils **25** *Hidden word:* Embittered
Ralph (*reversed*) **26** *Anagram:* saw knees

Down

1 *Double definition* **2** *Double definition* [Overthrows can cause extra runs
in cricket] **3** *Single definition* **4** *Single definition* **5** everyone separately =
EACH *within* circle = RING **6** politician = MP *within* lie (*anagram*)
7 certain = SURE *after* initial error = E + artist = RA **14** Present = OFFER +
conservative [Conservative] = TORY **15** *Single definition*
17 Drug = HEROIN + to end life = E **18** wander *without* direction =
ANDER *preceded by* ME **20** Got *reversed* + leg (*anagram*) **22** Final letters
[tails] of Hyderabad, Kashmir, Delhi, Rangoon, Bangkok

PUZZLE 2

Across

1 *Double definition* **9** concerning = OVER + condition = STATE
10 *Hidden word:* trainer tries **11** fashionable = IN + camping equipment =
TENT **12** Tree = ALDER + servant = MAN **13** Initially galloping =
G + ROUND **15** AS + indicated = SIGNED **18** Trick = CON + test =
TEMPT **19** Everyone = ALL *inside* holy men = STS **21** silent =
DUMB + ringer = BELL **23** A tissue *sounds like* 'Atishoo!' **26** Heather =
LING + love = O **27** person initially = P + dwelling = RESIDENT
28 *Anagram:* man so I report

Down

1 *Anagram:* rig, done **2** *Double definition* **3** *Anagram:* Cranes one
4 A girl = 'a lass' (*sounds like ...*) **5** Irritates = NEEDLES + skinhead = S
6 *Hidden word:* volcano is erupting **7** *Double definition* **8** Newspaperman =
ED *after* point-to-point = S TO N **14** OR + designate = NAME + part of the
Bible = NT **16** **11** *Ac* = INTENT + one on = ION **17** *Double definition*
18 old King = COLE *containing* 'learnéd' religious person = DD
20 Very thin = SHEER *containing* lieutenant = LT **22** bedroom *without*
little Edward = 'Ed' **24** *Hidden word:* delectable **25** *Alternate letters:*
Immerses

PUZZLE 3
Across
1 Russian = RED + vehicle = CAR **4** *Single definition* **9** *Single definition*
[deck = deck of cards] **11** *Anagram:* Merle **12** *Hidden word:* Is he a farmer
13 selling = peddling *sounds like ...* **15** *Hidden word:* need **17** *Single
definition:* [lights = blank squares] **20** to make a mistake = ERR + IF *within*
tide (*anagram*) **21** *Double definition* **23** Verse = CANTO + points =
N, E, S, E **25** Strange = RUM + graduate = BA **27** *Hidden word:*
mechanised **28** Draw on = INDUCE *containing* rot (*anagram*) **29** *Anagram:*
Terns go + South = 'S' **30** Girl = KATE *within* points = S, S

Down
1 *Single definition* **2** *Single definition* **3** *Anagram:* a terrific **5** All right =
OK *containing* A **6** *Double definition* **7** *Double definition* **8** second-hand =
SH + carpets = RUGS **10** better = IMPROVE *containing* IS
14 Disagreement = DISSENT *containing* ID **16** *Double definition*
18 *Single definition* **19** Common cold's = STREAMERS, *without* river = 'r'
22 fight = SCRAP + sickness initially = S **24** Gangs of witches =
COVENS *without* caught = 'c' **26** *Double definition*
28 Even = *even letters of* filches

PUZZLE 4
Across
1 *Double definition* **10** *Anagram:* Bite not as **11** Peril = 'danger'... almost
12 Bird = GULL + very last = Y **13** IN + new church = NCE *containing*
grief = DOLE **14** *Double definition* **16** *Quotation* **18** *Anagram:* twinge
containing the first time = T **20** TO + match = TALLY **21** automobiles
without wheels = 'autmbiles' (*anagram*) **23** manner *sounds like ...*
24 Former = EX + deed = ACT **25** A tragic + member = 'MP' (*anagram*)
26 To trick = CON + going down = DESCENDING

Down
2 rude = INSOLENT *containing* advocate's third letter = V
3 *Double definition* **4** organ = EAR *within* part of building = WING
5 *Anagram:* altered **6** *Double definition* **7** near gondola (*hidden word*)
8 Latzvian, for instance = TONGUE + tormentor = TWISTER **9** *Single
definition* **15** to instruct = INITIATE + leading driver = D **17** English town =
DARLINGTON *without* Head = 'D' **19** Lightweight = GRAM + Manx cat =
'puss' *less* 's' **20** Mostly generate = 'geneate'(*anagram*) **22** British = BR +
eggs = 'ova' *reversed* **23** *Single definition*

PUZZLE 5
Across
1 as tutee *without* point = 'e' **4** *Double definition* **9** *Anagram:* acre
10 Conservative = TORY *after* concert = PROM + in progress = ON
11 Disapproval expressed = BOO *containing* a doctor = AMB
12 *Single definition* ['beaten fairly and ...' = roundly beaten] **13** *Quotation*
15 *Double definition* **16** *Anagram:* Stop **17** *Anagram:* A lame bird
21 Note = B + Queen Elizabeth I = ERI *twice* **22** *Double definition*
24 C.I.A. *containing* Red Nell *(anagram)* **25** night owls often nap *(first letter of each word)* **26** *Sounds like* 'earnest' **27** *Anagram:* Master

Down
1 Noah's vessel = 'Ark' [a description of which might *sound* old-fashioned]
2 *Hidden word:* towpath robbers **3** *Anagram:* Oil spot **5** *Double definition*
6 *Anagram:* a fleet war **7** Rugby Union = RU + RALLY **8** West = W *after*
Beds = COTS + ancient = OLD + uplands = HILLS **14** duke = D + routed in
(anagram) **16** before = PRE + *sounds like* 'Miss' **18** motorway *reversed* =
IM + PLANT **19** the French = LE + husband = GROOM **20** *Hidden word:*
the art shop **23** *Double definition*

PUZZLE 6
Across
1 *Double definition* **8** *Double definition* **10** *Double definition* [Brown =
surname] **11** headless fish = 'brill' *minus* 'b' **13** Reveals *(anagram)*
15 Hush = SH + rude *sounds like* ... **16** Head [of] gunner = G *changes* to R
17 Grave need made + East = 'E' + Australian first = 'A' *(anagram)*
18 Prepare food = COOK + that is = IE **20** *Anagram:* leg and **21** Directions =
E,N + police = FORCE **22** back-tracking union = RUN ['NUR' *reversed*]
containing I **25** Dim intuition *minus* it **26** Shiite *without* a greeting ['hi']
27 *Double definition*

Down
2 *Hidden word:* Brahmin caste **3** Herb = 'thyme' *sounds like* ... **4** *Anagram:*
detour *with* 'o' *replacing* u **5** *Double definition* [Read 'Green keeper'] **6**
Initial letters: Lying upon my back and rubbing **7** Miss = GIRL + China =
FRIEND **9** Team up = ALLY *after* football club = ORIENT **12** Doctor =
MB *within* Troon + IS + the top = T **13** *Double definition* **14** *Double
definition* **15** Mussolini = 'Duce' *(anagram) inside* emotional pressure =
STRESS **19** *Single definition* [colourful way = green] **20** account = ACC +
application = USE **23** *Double definition* **24** *Hidden word:* a no-name

PUZZLE 7
Across

1 Fool one = ASSI *within* company = CO **5** tower = SPIRE *within* part of India = IND **9** *Initial letters:* All clues read over so that I can **10** *Hidden word:* roast enchilada **11** *Anagram:* farm plot **12** IN + church = CH + journalist = ED **13** *Single definition* [American word for normality] **15** *Single definition* **17** *Double definition* **19** *Anagram:* avoids + lines of communication = RY **20** *Substitute* 'e,e' *for first and last letters of* squats **21** *Single definition* ['In the velvet glove ...'] **22** island = IOM [Isle of Man] *within* hell = 'Dis' (*anagram*) **23** IS + A + beauty = BELLE **24** Late = NIGHT + pilot = FLY **25** 'terrors' *less initial letter*

Down

2 A revolting peasant = A CADE [Jack Cade, one of the leaders of the Peasants' Revolt] *containing* pass = COL **3** wine = PORT *within* shop = SING [criminal slang for inform] **4** DUCK = O + routed as (*anagram*) **5** *Double definition* **6** TEN *within* copy (*anagram*) **7** RAN + caught = C + Superman = HERO **8** *Anagram:* die-hard + left = 'L' **14** *Anagram:* Cool cheat **15** Check *sounds like* Czech... **16** Call up = RING *containing* inspiration = 'muse' *reversed* **17** *Anagram:* be hearty **18** *Single definition* [Cambridge graduate with first class degree in Mathematics] **19** A + non-drinker = TT *before* EMPT

PUZZLE 8
Across

1 Mineral = MICA *within* mountain pass = COL **5** desert *sounds like* 'dessert' **9** *Single definition* [lord's = Lord's cricket ground] **10** *Single definition* [heavyweight = 'heavy weight'] **11** *Double definition* **13** bearings = S,ES *containing* lock = TRESS **15** *Double definition* **16** MAY *containing* number initially = N **18** *Single definition* **19** Translator = TR *within* SADDLING **22** *Anagram:* lancing a **23** public money = FINANCE *removing* 'n' **25** *First letters:* under frying oil **26** *Double definition* **28** *Anagram:* Ensured **29** Really = INDEED *containing* unknown quantity = X

Down

1 Mozart, for example = COMPOSER *removing* right = 'r' **2** *Hidden word:* Bermuda **3** Copper = CU + can = ABLE *containing* record = LP **4** old pianist = 'Liszt' *sounds like* ...[old refers to both pianist and solution] **5** *Anagram:* Accurate + directions = 'S,N' **6** *Hidden word:* Rustles up perhaps **7** AT + trial = TEST + relation *without* 'rel' **8** *Double definition* **12** *Single definition* **14** Engineers = RES + coach = TRAINER **17** *Anagram:* dace + half tiddlers = 'tidd' **18** *Double definition* **20** Relieved = EASED *after* short Greek = GR **21** *Double definition* [Cockney eyes = 'mince pies'] **24** Each = PER + one = I **27** *Double definition*

PUZZLE 9
Across
1 advance payment = SUB + teams = SIDES **5** *Single definition* **10** *Double definition* **11** *Double definition* [squeezed = compressed – no hyphen in compound solution] **12** *Anagram:* danger + Eastern = 'E' **13** *Hidden word:* Baghdad no canard (*reversed*) **15** Complete = 'lot' (*reversed*) *containing* army reserves = 'TA' [Definition is also Complete] **17** *Double definition* **19** *Anagram:* acid near **22** *Single definition* [Reference to **7Dn**] **23** *Hidden word:* Tripos term **24** *Single definition* **25** *Single definition* [You might 'set tee' before you drive off in golf] **26** *Double definition* [Ignore comma to read 'Small fleet']

Down
1 None *sounds like* 'nun'... **2** *Single definition* **3** fool = IDIOT + in charge = IC **4** *Anagram:* there **6** sailor = AB + REST *containing* A **7** Endure = STAND + punishment = STOCKS + to the point that = TILL **8** *Anagram:* Duly send **9** *Double definition* [one who's in = batsman; a batsman can take guard on off stump – though this is not usual] **14** ran back = NAR + desert = RAT + gold = OR **16** *Double definition* **18** *Double definition* **20** *Single definition* [Cleopatra's life came to a halt because of an asp] **21** *Double definition* [For I ran, read 'Iran'] **23** Two boys = ROY + AL

PUZZLE 10
Across
1 Wrench *with* the top = 't' *substituted at the beginning* **4** *Anagram:* A trapper **10** *Hidden word:* put her Malcolm **11** Girl = MAY + spoken = ORAL **12** Listens again = REHEARS + one = I + no good initially = NG **13** *Anagram:* sink [Reference to **4 Ac**] **15** Suspend = HANG + boxer = DOG **17** Picture = SHOT + set = PUT **19** Problem originating = P + at the back = ASTERN **21** *Anagram:* Roam pie **23** *Double definition* **24** *Anagram:* queues + at + Street = 'St' **27** Little = MINI + *reference to* 'Malcolm' *(abbreviated)* **28** Knot = TIE + attaches = PINS **29** *Anagram:* Any chits **30** *Single definition*

Down
1 Teachers' = TUTORS + joint = HIP **2** *Anagram:* nowhere [Samuel Butler's novel of that name] **3** animals = DEER *after* public land = 'common' *sounds like ...* **5** *Anagram:* nice mires **6** *Anagram:* a spy **7** Score = PAR + cut = SNIP **8** *Double definition* **9** Low = 'moo' + south-east = 'se' [Solution = European species of moose] **14** *Double definition* **16** Information = GEN + Italians' *less* 'ns' **18** Stanza = VERSE *within* Arts (*anagram*) **20** *Initial letters:* Spruce, poplar, ironwood, nutmeg, nicotinia, elder, yew **22** Religious Education = RE + old choir = QUIRE **23** Companies = COS *containing* medical graduate = MB **25** *Single definition* [Tate Gallery named after Sir Henry Tate, sugar refiner and philanthropist] **26** *Hidden word:* Ham and *reversed*

PUZZLE 11
Across
1 *Single definition* **4 & 2 Dn** Ship's officer = CAPTAIN + Welsh town = FLINT [Long John Silver's parrot in *Treasure Island*] **9** golden rule = 'principle', *sounds like* ... **10** becomes end of = S + handle = HAFT **11** *Double definition* **12** *Quotation* **13** former = EX + corsair = 'pirate' *less* resistance = 'r' **15** one (*anagram*) + BE *containing* right = R **17** IN + explosive = TNT *containing* energy = E **19** *Anagram:* a + National Trust = 'NT' + tree (*anagram*) **22** Furnish = PROVIDE + books = NT **24** *Anagram:* resistance unit = 'ohm' + ack-ack = 'aa' **26** *Hidden word:* soprano is exquisite **27** *Anagram:* Take choir **28** *Single definition* [climbers = climbing plants] **29** Lost = 'astray' *containing* hot tip = 'h'

Down
1 island = CAPRI + church = CE **2** *See 4 Ac* **3** Old = EX + chief officer = CO + irate (*anagram*) **4** pass = COL + LATE [Passover = 'pass over', get-together = 'get together'] **5** Dad's = PAS + gratitude = TA **6** Girl = ADA + exercise = PT + fit = ABLE **7** NOT + A + line = RY **8** Work = OP + I + took in = ATE **14** Peter = PAN + TO + act silently = MIME **16** Withdraws = RETRACTS *containing* nothing = O **18** *Anagram:* space to **19** entirety *less* note = 're' **20** Attempt = TRY *containing* chase = RACE **21** *Anagram:* Pest in **23** *Double definition* **25** Othello = 'a Moor', *sounds like* ...

PUZZLE 12
Across
1 *Abbreviation of* 'spectacles' *sounds like* ... **5** cab *reversed* = BAC + CAR + AT **9** *Double definition* **10** *Hidden word:* metal is sometimes **11** *Single definition* [eye sounds like 'I'] **12** *Double definition* **13** Frenchman = 'M' *contained in* grenade (*anagram*) **15** leads a double life = 'is' *repeated* **17** lavish = 'plush' *take away final* 'h' **19** salesman = 'rep' (*anagram*) + pain = ACHE + right = R **20** Emphatic opening = EM + gambit = PLOY **21** a pure one (*anagram*) [Reference to **13 Ac**] **22** Many = M + Ravel (*anagram*) **23** *Double definition* **24** *Anagram:* true saint *without* 'e' **25** *Double definition*

Down
2 *Anagram:* a rap song **3** animals = COWS *containing* heather = LING **4** *Anagram:* steer horn **5** *Single definition* **6** *Anagram:* since he [Boxer = member of Chinese secret society] **7** Store's closing = RES + I + two = DUAL **8** Hardy heroine = TESS *containing* to end prayer = AMEN **14** Graduate = MA + to express suspicion = HA + Indian landlord = RAJAH **15** [Another Crimean War battle – see **5 Ac**] **16** Fashionable = IN + drink = SPIRIT **17** *Anagram:* red paper **18** *Anagram:* ten fauns **19** ONE *within* jetty = PIER

PUZZLE 13
Across

1 *Double definition* **4** *Single definition* [after dinner invitation = 'after-dinner invitation'] **10** *Double definition* [Louis XV's mistress gave her name to a raised hairstyle] **11** Hold back = DAM *containing* about = RE **12** soldier = ANT + run away = ELOPE **13** *Single definition* **15** *Hidden word:* The aching **17** Put in grave = INTER + appearance = VIEW **20** *Double definition* **21** Hidden word: from entrails **24** A + second = S + conveyed = SENT **25** Company = CO + papers = PRESS *containing* Maxwell's initial = M **28** AREA *containing* centre of Genoa = N **29** *Anagram:* cedar tree **30** *Single definition* **31** A + churchman = DD + started = LED

Down

1 *Anagram:* parcel Ed **2** Reach = COME + tiptop = T **3** about = RE + League member = ALLY **5** tune = AIR + funny ending = Y **6** *Anagram:* deviates **7** Finished = OVER + wearing original = W + headger = HELM **8** TO + atom (*anagram*) **9** *Single definition* [hole sounds like 'whole'] **14** control = REIN + FOR + the Church = CE **16** *Single definition* **18** *Double definition* [Pole = 'pole'] **19** *Double definition* **22** Best start = B + pineapple = ANANAS *less* second = 's' **23** *Double definition* **26** Former = EX + charge = 'toll', *sounds like* ... **27** Support = BRA + model = T

PUZZLE 14
Across

1 *Single definition* **8** large sums of money = 'pots' (*reversed*) **10** *Single definition* [Tacky describes tacking, i.e. going across] **11** a variety of paints = 'oils' (*anagram*) **13** File = LIST *within* information = GEN **15** *Double definition* [Read 'Going up/stairs'] **16** *Initial letters:* Rossini, Offenbach, Nielsen, Debussy, Orff, Schoenberg **17** *Anagram:* a dream has a charm **18** *Double definition* **20** refusal = NO + race = TT *within* Kentucky = KY **21** *Anagram:* Paying *containing* quiet = 'p' **22** *Anagram:* Roman *less* article = 'a' **25** *Double definition* [*Take away* 'in' from description of persistent offender **26** *Hidden word:* say a mantra (*reversed*) **27** *Anagram:* the saint is

Down

2 *Double definition* **3** right = R *within* advice = TIP **4** *Anagram:* Ulster **5** *Single definition* [present = gift] **6** points = E, S, S, E *within* two sides = L, R **7** *Anagram:* Shot purely **9** *Double definition* **12** *Anagram:* fed by prior **13** *Double definition* [Reference to *A Christmas Carol*] **14** *Double definition* ['... Full of sound and fury Signifying ...'] **15** *Single definition* [Reference to syndicate members at Lloyds] **19** *Double definition* [Douglas made an aircraft named after these two states] **20** *Anagram:* Thing + King = 'k' **23** Napoleon's island = ELBA (*reversed*) **24** still = YET + single = I

PUZZLE 15
Across
1 *Historical reference* [Old and Young Pretenders] **6** *Hidden word:* physics laboratory **10** *Initial letters:* often can taste of pretty unpalatable stuff **11** Literary reference [Spoonerism: 'nook and cranny'] **12** river = 'Exe' + trips *(anagram)* + East = E **13** girl's head = 'g' *within* rough = 'rude' [Eponymous hero of Dickens novel] **14** *Anagram:* La Mer **15** *Anagram:* as it is fed **17** loved = DOTED *containing* bird = MINA **20** 'r' *removed from* 'rotter' **21** by *sounds like* 'bye' **23** *Anagram:* Gall and + urethra opening = 'ur' **25** *Double definition* [Indian refers to ink] **26** Beat = TAN + chap = GENT **27** *Double definition* **28** A French = UN + action = DEED *containing* exploit = FEAT

Down
1 Soft = P + dress = ROBE **2** *Anagram:* contemplates *taking away* net **3** Former = EX + fairy = PERI + psychically = MENTALLY **4** infernal = DIS + American waitress = MISS **5** when finally = N + the way up = ASCENT **7** *Anagram* Idle + partner = 'N' **8** Exchange goods = BARTER *containing* END **9** *Anagram:* prose concerned **14** *Double definition* **16** *Quotation* **18** directions = E,N *after* drunk = TIGHT **19** river = DEE *containing* RAFT **22** *Anagram:* Knot *containing* end of tie = E **24** *Anagram:* Trade

PUZZLE 16
Across
1 *Double definition* **4** *Anagram:* acres *within* DEED **9** *Single definition* [Snow White should be read 'snow white'; the solution may be thought of as somewhat poetic] **10** exercise = PE *containing* RON [On the contrary refers to indication: clue should read 'Exercise taking Ron'] **11** *Hidden word:* token listening **12** *Anagram:* Treaders **14, 16, 22 Dn**, **29 Ac, 6 Dn** war story *sounds like* 'Waugh' story + early Italian state = ROMAN EMPIRE **16** *See* **14 Ac** **19** *Anagram:* Odes **20** *Anagram:* Wobble *containing* note = 'F' **22** Oddly having lost five hundred = ODLY *containing* debts = IOUS **23** *Double definition* **26** small Italian restaurant = TRAT *containing* one = I **27** levels = STRATA + stone = GEM **28** about = 're' (anagram) *within* tax = EXCISE + demand initially = D **29** *See* **14 Ac**

Down
1 With Italian = CON + nurse = TEND + Edward = ED **2** *Take away:* trainee = 'l' from do well **3** *Double definition* **4** cull *substituting* D for 'c' [one hundred + four hundred in Roman numerals] **5** *Single definition* [By sounds like 'bi' ...] **6** *See* **14 Ac** **7** Brief = SHORT + dip = FALL **8** *Hidden word:* cadre a democracy **13** *Anagram:* their slabs **15** Actors = CAST + one = I + entrance = GATE **17** sound coming from manger = LOW + manger *(anagram)* **18** *Double definition* **21** Brown = RUST + in charge = IC **22** *See* **14 Ac** **24** *Double definition* **25** food = 'bread', *sounds like ...*

PUZZLE 17

Across

1 *Single definition* [paid driver] **6** the old way = WISE + right = R **9** *Single definition* [High sounds like 'Hi!'] **10** SHE *containing* 'too' *backwards* **11** *Double definition* **13** *Single definition* **14** Battled = 'fought', *sounds like* ... **16** sweetheart = E *within* chap = MAN **17** *Anagram:* such tinted **19** Conservative = C + Bar = LEVER + hesitate = ER **20** not fresh = OFF + apt *(anagram)* **23** highly valued = PRECIOUS *containing* company = CO + issue = CHILD **24** *Double definition* **25** *Anagram:* A Green right (= 'r') to

Down

1 Quotes = 'cites' *sounds like* ... **2** relevant = APPROPRIATE + points = N,E,S,S **3** *Anagram:* the stiff **4** Leader of Hallé = H *within* English Chamber Orchestra = ECO **5** *Anagram:* Enumerate + initial requirements = 'r' **6** *Double definition* **7** *Single definition* [Extremely = at the end] **8** your last = R + bird = EGRET + Edward = ED **12** Top botanist = B + down = UNDER *within* heather = LING **13** *Double definition* **15** *Double definition* [Description refers to the job of a paid driver] **18** *Double definition* [form = class] **21** *Single definition* **22** Scottish poet = 'Burns' *without final* 's'

PUZZLE 18

Across

1 *Single definition* ['commonly' has connotation of Commons where members = 'Members' sit] **4** *Anagram:* Crude SAS **10** TO + old pipe *(anagram)* **11** *Hidden word:* silent a citizen's **12** Gustav = HOLST + hesitation = ER **13** *Anagram:* it veers **14** *Single definition* **15** hits back and forth = 'raps' *(reversed)* + TANS **18** *Hidden word:* Thunderous sea unusual **20** A + quiet = P + friend = PAL **23** *Anagram:* rig vote **25** *Double definition* [bed = flower bed] **26** *Anagram:* means **27** Conversation = TALK + 'native' without 'n' **28** *Single definition* [house = House] **29** present = AD + times = AGES

Down

1 *Double definition* [Wagner's opera] **2** BOILER *containing* right = R **3** Archer's = TELLS *containing* story = TALE **5** Outstanding = SUPER + of course = NATURALLY **6** consumed = ATE *within* the outskirts of Damascus = D,S **7** *Single definition* [Removing 'man' from **1** *Dn* and combining what remains with this solution gives an expression for a sale where prices are lowered until a buyer is found] **8** *Anagram:* Tester **9** cricket's = SPORTS + about = RE + drink = PORTER **16** Prepare = TRAIN + group = BAND **17** *Quotation* [*Ode on a Distant Prospect of Eton College*] **19** *Single definition* [Crewe *sounds like* 'crew' ...] **21** suffering = PAYING *containing* right = R **22** First lady's = EVES *containing* not disheartened = NT **24** *Double definition* [IN ... secondary definition is run together]

PUZZLE 19
Across

1 *Single definition* [Main = connection with sea] **9** *Literary reference* [Darlings' dog in *Peter Pan*] **10** *Double definition* [an 'S' = ans, in other words abbreviation of 'answer'] **11** *Hidden word:* Bach if I **14** *Double definition* **16** *Anagram:* React + partner = 'E' **17** RED *containing* soldier = MAN **18** An extra = 'A leg-bye' *(abbreviation)* **20** *Anagram:* recasts **21** love = O + bites *(anagram)* + may ultimately = Y **22** *Literary reference* [Book title] **24** *Anagram:* Men are **26** Georgia = GA + tea *(anagram)* + fashionable = U **27** conservative = C *within* footwear = SANDAL **28** *Double definition* **31** performing = DANCING = nude + 'bare', *sounds like ...*] **32** Lion family = 'pride' *less first letter* **33** *Single definition*

Down

2 *Single definition* **3** gold = OR *within* street = ST **4** hounded = 'chased', *sounds like ...* **5** *Single definition* [bridge = bridge of nose] **6** bird = SKUA, *sounds like ...* **7** *Single definition* **8** *Miscellaneous* [Sat = 'Saturday' = DAY + IN + sun = 'Sunday' = DAY + abroad = OUT **12** *Anagram:* Former panel **13** *Single definition* **14** Mists = STEAMS *containing* river condensed = R **15** novel = NEW *within* genuine = REAL **18** *Hidden word:* crevasse **19** *Odd letters:* booty **23** *Anagram:* a pea can **25** *Move last letter of* Claire *to first position* **26** *Anagram:* Arrange *without* article = 'a' **29** Mabel *without first letter* **30** BAR + key = E

PUZZLE 20
Across

1 Individual = UNIT *containing* student = L **4** oriental = E + woman who is fascinating = WITCH *within* BED **9** *Single definition* [Victory = HMS *Victory*] **10** Dog = 'Airedale' *without final letters* **11** Not in = OUT + suitable = FIT **12** Leave vehicle = PARK + road = LANE **14** *Single definition* **16** before = 'ante' *reversed* **19** *Anagram:* snag **20** Fluid = WATER + runs = WORKS **22** *Double definition* **23** *Anagram:* A paper **26** *Double definition* [Novel by Graham Greene] **27** Might = MAIN + publish = ISSUE **28** scrap of cloth = RAG *within* France **29** *Hidden word:* rogue's strategy

Down

1 copper = 'd' + turned on *(anagram)* [New is the definition] **2** fast = LENT *sounds like ...* **3** *Single definition* [The full title of *Romeo and Juliet*] **4** *Double definition* **5** Licence = WARRANT + that is = IE + partner = S **6** *Anagram:* carts *containing* the middle of Carrickfergus = 'ck' **7** *Quotation* **8** *Anagram:* Odd + for example = 'eg' **13** *Anagram:* Remain + calm **15** *Single definition* [Plate = River Plate, mainly = by the sea] **17** *Miscellaneous* [Solution is combined with 'shock'] **18** Partner = S + somewhere in the East End = WAPPING **21** *Double definition* [Spinner = 'arachnid'; also a long-legged snooker rest] **22** French word = MOT + IF **24** Directions = EN + girl = SUE **25** German wine = 'Wein', *sounds like ...*

PUZZLE 21
Across
1 *Single definition* **9** *Anagram:* Might oral **10** No + taxi = 'cab' *(reversed)*
11 *Single definition* [Usually abbreviated to 'ult.'] **12** Help = TEND +
measure = EN + extremes of company = CY **14** Small particle = ATOM +
I *within* canal *(anagram)* **16** animal doctor = VET + duck = O **18** *Hidden
word:* endorsing evangelism [The gloomy dean in the solution is quite
common in crosswords!] **19** S*ingle definition* [Type of biscuit] **21** *Anagram:*
August V [= 5] *containing* Sweden = 'S' **22** *Anagram:* Go if an [Juan
Manuel, world motor racing champion] **25** Not out = IN + US + note = E
26 *Single definition* [board = table] **27** *Single definition*

Down
1 Working out = CALCULATING + object = MIND **2** Small contribution =
'mite', *sounds like* ... **3** Flash = DART + room *reversed* = MOOR **4** *Double
definition* **5** Moderate = TEMPER + A + northern church = NCE
6 foundations = BEDS *following* measurement = EM **7** *Single definition*
[Bill implies 'telephone bill'] **8** *Single definition* **13** *Anagram:* Fires built
15 *Single definition* **17** *Double definition* **20** [Two different words for perform]
23 Country = 'Ghana', *sounds like* ... **24** No = O + *synonym of* **16** *Ac*

PUZZLE 22
Across
1 Dismiss = SACK + priests = CLOTH **6** *Anagram:* Beat's [Old word
for beat] **9** *Hidden word:* latent heat retained [For crucible, read 'Crucible' –
theatre in Sheffield] **10** Othello = MOOR + home = IN + midnight = G
11 *Anagram:* inert **12** Counter = BAR + measure = METER *containing*
nothing = O **14** *Anagram:* fort *minus* 'f' **15** *Anagram:* as cure's near **17** Eye
queue *sounds like* ... IQ **19** Fool = 'sap' *reversed* **20** *Anagram:* in the gloom
minus East = 'E' **22** One = I + kind of wood = DEAL **24** *Single definition*
26 *Single definition* [For not intent, read 'not in tent', i.e. out in the open]
27 Surely *minus* equanimity initially = 'e' **28** *Double definition*

Down
1 seating *minus* for example = 'eg' **2** *Anagram:* reactor [He with capital 'H']
3 *Single definition* [For Aspire ... in the City, read 'A spire ... in the city']
4 about = OVER + position = BEARING **5** Hamlet *minus* allow [= 'let']
6 *Double definition* **7** small = S + glove = MITTEN **8** Keen = EAGER +
Head = NESS **13** *Anagram:* creeps + board = TABLE **14** *Double definition*
16 *Anagram:* Terrier + vet almost = 've' **18** stagger = TOTTER *containing*
run = 'r' **19** Power to begin = P + begin again = RESUME **21** *Anagram:*
Italy **23** *Anagram:* ludic **25** Gains *minus* 'in'

PUZZLE 23
Across
1 a payment = 'a cost', *sounds like* ... **4** Nowadays = AD + junta *(anagram)* + second staff = T [Definition also part of device] **10** *Single definition* [of the fields in French] **11** to finish trial = L + recess = apse **12** to draw = TIE + explorer = POLO **13** noted = RE + stories = 'tales', *sounds like* ... **14** *Double definition* [Type of hair treatment] **15** *Anagram:* elements **18** *Single definition* **20** *Initial letters:* plebeian leaders as top orators **23** *Single definition* **25** *Anagram:* me to her **26** *Single definition* **27** Pointed = E + proposal = MOTION + gangster = AL [Capone] **28** I object = ME + on board = SS + friend = MATE [Definition also part of device] **29** Engineers = REME + defy extremes = DY

Down
1 *Single definition* **2** strict order = 'Cistercian' *less* CIA **3** *Double definition* **5** *Single definition* [Orpheus went down to the Underworld = DIS] **6** *Anagram:* until **7** A + soft = P + tip = POINT **8** Article = THE + first = IST **9** *Anagram:* Irishmen vote + Prime Minister = 'PM' **16** *Double definition* [Dam *sounds like* 'damn'] **17** *Hidden word:* [in]form all youngsters **19** *Single definition* [Soldiers = pieces of toast] **21** Called = RANG *within* time = 'era' *(reversed)* **22** Make a killing = 'murder' *(reversed)* **24** *Reverse:* Muesli *less* 's'

PUZZLE 24
Across
1 *Double definition* **4** plant = CRESS + mountain = IDA [Reference to Shakespeare/Chaucer/Homer lovers] **10** *Anagram:* Chairs get **11** *Hidden word:* Rossetti described **12** *Literary reference* [*How they brought the Good News from Ghent to Aix*] **13** *Anagram:* lout is + King = 'r' **14** *Anagram:* Naive **15** *Anagram:* named tea **18** sweets = 'desserts' *(reversed)* **20** Noticed = SEEN *containing* Hancock first = H **23** *Double definition* **25** old Spanish coin = REAL + looks *sounds like* 'eyes' **26** *Anagram:* tunnel *without* north = 'n' **27** *Double definition* **28** *Anagram:* foster + line = RY **29** doctor = SURGEON *less first letter*

Down
1 *Anagram:* in G Sharp **2** *Double definition* **3** *Double definition* **5** *Single definition* [Sinister is connected with the left hand] **6** *Double definition* **7** *Anagram:* Guildenstern *without* back [= 'stern'] **8** donkey = ASS + first = IST **9** profligate = SPENDER *preceded by* king = STEPHEN [Spender edited the magazine *Encounter*] **16** *Take away* [farewell] a final = a ending *from* attending *to leave* 'TT' = 'teetotaller' [This is a briefly glimpsed indication of the solution] **17** *Anagram:* bun + consumed = EATEN **19** *Double definition* **21** Unfinished epic = EPI + novel, for example = TOME **22** Scratch = SCUFF *containing* right = R **24** *Single definition* [Allusion is to swearing 'by ...']

PUZZLE 25
Across

1 *Double definition* **9** *Initial letters:* usually regarded as less steep
10 *Anagram:* River rose **11** *Double definition* **12** *Hidden word:* stalk aligns
14 left = L *within* regret = RUE **15** direction = S *within* aggrieves *(anagram)*
18 International body = UN + support = STAND *containing* German article =
DER **19** *Double definition* **21** *Single definition* **23** *Single definition* [blue,
red = corners in boxing match] **25** *Hidden word (reversed):* seat a Roman is
26 *Double definition* **27** *Anagram:* station register

Down

1 *Single definition* [Self-defence in boxing] **2** *Miscellaneous* ['Well-' if
connected to solution = cosmopolitan] **3** *Single definition* [Latin for on the
spot] **4** *Single definition* [plot = garden] **5** *Double definition* **6** shapeless =
'formless' *substitute* 'g' *for first letter* **7** A + European capital = ROMA
8 *Double definition* **13** *Double definition* [Operation] **16** Italian = IT +
tanner I *(anagram)* **17** *Anagram:* part + exit = DOOR **20** South African =
BOER *containing* doctor = MB [WW2 bomber] **22** A + quantity = MASS
24 cheese = 'Edam' *reversed*

PUZZLE 26
Across

1 Clothing = DRESS *containing* acceptable = U **4** Whereby Roman =
QUA + locomotive = TRAIN **10** *Miscellaneous* [Michaelangelo is the
Renaissance man] **11** Drink *(anagram)* + editor = ED **12** *Single definition*
[Both climbing plants and employees can be redirected by doing this]
13 cross = 'rood' *(reversed)* **15** accessory = ADD ON *containing* IS
[Addison was the original co-publisher of *The Spectator* magazine]
17 directions = EN + count, for example = TITLE **19** *Single definition* [Grey
sounds like 'Gray', the poet] **21** Scores = TRIES + depleted team = TE
23 *Hidden word:* send up eternal **24** No words = MIME + no = O + picture =
GRAPH **27** Boy = DICK *containing* stray = ERR **28** mean = CHEAP +
measure = EN **29** *Single definition* ['nightlife' *sounds like* 'knight life']
30 entry = 'ingress', *take away* 's'

Down

1 *Anagram* create dam **2** to name = CITE *within* colour = RED
3 Mariner's = SEAMANS + joint = HIP **5** *Quotation* [Shakespeare's
Julius Caesar] **6** Fish = 'tuna' *(anagram)* **7** Broadcast = AIR + left = PORT
[where you might view wings] **8** *Hidden word:* in a dire **9** *Single definition*
[Reference to **11** *Ac*] **14** *Anagram:* Brings neat **16** *Single definition* ['nits' –
unwelcome visitors – are sometimes found in children's hair] **18** hunter =
[John] 'Peel' *(anagram)* + somewhere in the South of England = HANTS
20 *Anagram:* Rome, pre **22** knave = SCAMP + king = ER
23 *Double definition* **25** *Initial letters:* exposes all cards held
26 *Reference to* **11** *Ac containing* left = L

PUZZLE 27

Across

1 *Double definition* **6** Accountant = CA + politician = MP
10 *Quotation* ['Men seldom make passes ...' (Attributed to Dorothy Parker)]
11 hairdo = PERM *containing* FOR **12** flower = ELITE *containing* bird = MINA **13** poles = N,S *within* river = DEE **14** *Hidden word:* [part-]time qualification **15** *Anagram:* Hastens + directions = 'E,E' **17** Fertile = GREEN + region = LAND **20** One = I + the French Prime Minister = LE PM *(reversed)* **21** Small girl = DI *within* 'ran' *(reversed)* **23** A fight = A BOUT *preceded by* prison = STIR [Anglo-Irish word for porridge] **25** *Anagram:* man-eater *minus* 'r' **26** idle = LAZE *containing* here in France = ICI [Definition also part of device] **27** *Initial letters:* salute a new era **28** *Anagram:* Enter nice + park = 'P'

Down

1 Keen = 'eager', *sounds like...* [A tidal bore on the Severn] **2** President = P + carte blanche = LATITUDE [American term for cliché is drugstore philosophy] **3** Peter, for example, = 'disciple' [lacking final direction = *minus* 'e'] + IN + heretical = ARIAN **4** to try = TEST + tea *(anagram)* **5** *Anagram:* He pours **7** A seed = A CORN **8** *Single definition* [The eponymous hero of the adventure by Baroness Orczy] **9** *Single definition* **14** trains = ENGINES *containing* royal passenger = ER **16** Former = EX + terrorists = PLO + SON *containing* one = I **18** Gold = AU + reset *(anagram)* **19** Bird flying up = DRIB + allowed = LET **22** *Anagram* [Reference to solution of **21 Ac**] **24** article = THE + I object = ME

PUZZLE 28

Across

1 Fugitive = 'refugee' *minus* point = 'E' **4** *Double definition*
10 *Double definition* **11** stutterer *minus* way = 'st' *and* royal = 'ER'
12 love = O + lied *(anagram)* **13** End = TAIL + bit = PIECE [Design at the bottom of a page or chapter] **14** *Anagram:* They cared about **18** language = TURKISH + from France = DE + blonde = LIGHT **20** *Single definition* ['box' = hedge] **22** A + fit of bad temper = BATE **24** *Double definition* **25** *Anagram:* Sends one *preceded by* born = NEE **26** Class = FORM + too soon = 'early', *sounds like ...* **27** *Double definition*

Down

1 professional = PRO *within* range = REACH **2** friend *less* partner = 'N' **3** Good Scottish = GUID + publication = BOOK *containing* English = E **5** *Double definition* **6** first from the = T + bottom = RUMP **7** Issue = LITTER + concealed microphone = BUG **8** old vessel = ARK *within* study = DEN **9** *Single definition* **15** four out of 6 = TRUM [reference to **6 Dn**] + safe = PETER **16** lecture = TALK + musical = 'Evita' *(reversed)* **17** importance = STRESS + senior journalist = ED **19** *Miscellaneous* [By ... = alone] **21** *Anagram:* Eager **23** *Double definition*

PUZZLE 29
Across
1 right = R *within* tent = CAMP **4** *Single definition* [main = 'sea'] **9** *Double definition* [From book by Thomas Hobbes] **10** *Double definition* **11** South African = SA + instrument = LUTE **12** *Anagram:* start rehearsal = 'r' + no score **14** *Double definition* **16** *Double definition* **19** to judge = 'deem' *(reversed)* **20** *Single definition* [naval *sounds like* 'navel'] **22** *Anagram:* Carves + 's,e' [*initial letters of* skiing enthusiasts] **23** *Single definition* [reads *sounds like* 'reeds'] **26** Painter = RA + Edward = TED **27** *Single definition* [King Arthur's sword] **28** old boy = OB + LIED *containing* pistol = GAT **29** *Single definition*

Down
1 company = CO + LOSS + Emu *(anagram)* **2** *Hidden word:* Devonian village **3** Evaluate = PRICE *containing* some scenes = ACT **4** Such = SO + laughter heard = HO **5** *Anagram:* Grant only + one = 'i' **6** *Single definition* [bats = 'cricket bats'] **7** effort = 'exertion' *(misplaced letters) containing* key = 'C' **8** *Quotation* [*The Ballad of Reading Gaol*] **13** fools = ASSES + street = ST *containing* MEN **15** Three consecutive letters *sound like* EL ['L'] + EM ['M'] + EN ['N'] + totally at the heart = TAL **17** Choose = ELECT + examination = ORAL **18** strange = ODD + spheres = BALLS **21** drink = LAP + follow = DOG **22** Transport = CAR + depart = GO **24** Sad confession = 'I'm blue' *less* novice = 'L' **25** addiction first = A + detectives = CID

PUZZLE 30
Across
1 City = EC [postal district] + at a standstill = STATIC [transport = transport of delight] **6** domestic duty = 'mopping' *without* page = 'p' **9** a map back = PAMA *containing* AN **10** *Anagram:* Trap *containing* engineers = 'RE' *(reversed)* + in **11** young ox = STEER + grow old = AGE **12** Walker = 'rambler' *less first letter* **13** text = 'script' *less last letter* **14** *Anagram:* mental + in + East = E **17** *Anagram:* remain + ark **19** *Single definition* **22** French article that = UN QUE *containing* I **23** *Single definition* [Refers to *Book of Revelations*] **24** Greek character = PHI *within* great *(anagram)* [Lead refers to pencil-lead] **25** noted = D, E, F + article = A + I object = ME **26** *Anagram:* firm's first = 'f' + universal = 'u' + rule **27** *Double definition* [American word for beats; also means old records (players) which were made of this]

Down
2 tea = CHA + circle = O + citizen briefly = 'cit' *(reversed)* **3** *Anagram:* Great Dani **4** *Single definition* **5** *Single definition* [The ruler, the theme of **4** *Dn*, is CATHERINE the Great; mobilized support = WHEELS.] **6** *Single definition* ['Peg'] **7** disobedient child = IMP + fashionable = U + University = LSE **8** classes = GENERA + hill = TOR **13** *Anagram:* Surgeon *containing* credit = 'cr' [cut out = delete 'edit' from credit] **15** *Anagram:* Fluster a + maiden = 'm' **16** *Double definition* [Significant evidence at a trial] **18** *Hidden word:* limit at end **20** *Single definition* [Count = Dracula] **21** trains = BR + aren't working = IDLE

Solutions

It is standard practice with puzzle solutions not to indicate word divisions –
except for hyphens, which are shown by a short horizontal bar between one
square and the next.

Spelling conventions are always determined by the structure of the clue: the
setters must ensure that any solution with variant spellings is clued so that
only one of the variants is correct. Note that in our own puzzles, the variant
-*ize* is standard (in a word such as REALIZE); you will find, however, that
puzzles in daily papers prefer mainly the -*ise* variant (REALISE), which is
easier to clue, especially in anagrams.

1

3

2

4

5

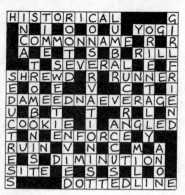

6

7

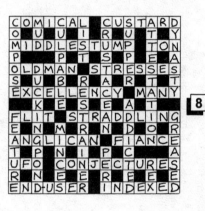

8

9

10

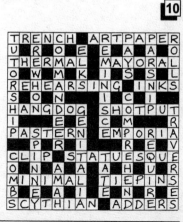

11

12

 13

14

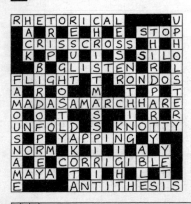

15

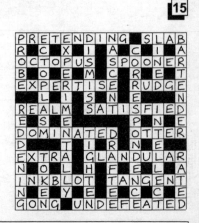

16

17

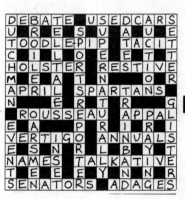

18

19

20

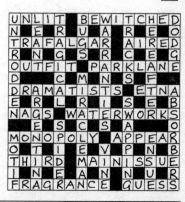

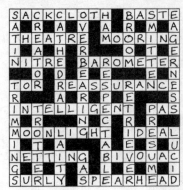

21

22

23

24

25

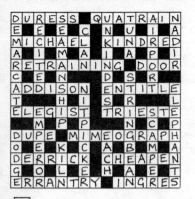

26

27

28

29

30

Further Reading and Contacts

Recommended Dictionaries
For most crossword enthusiasts, *Chambers Dictionary* is the recommended single-volume reference. It contains an enormous number of words not to be found in most other dictionaries and is essential for those wishing to progress to really advanced cryptic puzzles. It also has very useful supplements of abbreviations and first names. The only disadvantage of *Chambers* is that it does not contain encyclopedic entries. If you want a dictionary with such entries, *Chambers Encyclopedic English Dictionary* is the best choice: it meets most of the vocabulary requirements of ordinary daily paper cryptics.

Other Reference Sources
An atlas such as *The Times Concise Atlas* is useful, as is *Brewer's Dictionary of Phrase and Fable* (Cassell) – a mine of recondite information. *Larousse Dictionary of Literary Characters* is an excellent source for pinning down elusive references to the various literary classics which crossword-setters frequently assume we have all read. Another important means of solving literary clues is the quotation dictionary: *The Oxford Dictionary of Quotations* is the best.

A thesaurus can be very useful – both the original thematic *Roget's* (Penguin publish this in paperback) and the newer alphabetical type, which is more accurately described as a 'synonym dictionary'. *Longman's Synonym Dictionary* is probably the most complete, although the best value for money is offered in paperback by *Harrap's Dictionary of English Synonyms*.

Crossword 'Cribs'
Never be ashamed of using these: all the setters do! There are a lot available: Chambers publish *Anagrams, Back-Words, Words* and the *Crossword Completer*. The last-mentioned alphabetically lists alternate letters of words from 4 - 15 letters in length.

Other useful crossword references include *The Crossword Phrase Dictionary* (published by Stanley Paul), *The Complete Crossword Companion* by Jeremy Howard-Williams (Grafton) and two books by J.A. Coleman – his *Crossword Dictionary* and *The Complete Guide to Cryptic Crosswords* – both published by Collins.

Books on Crosswords
Unfortunately, many of the classic works are out of print and difficult to obtain. This includes *Ximenes on the Art of the Crossword* by D.S. Macnutt – one of the definitive books on cryptics – and May Abbott's *How to do Crosswords Better* (Collins). The most complete introduction and guide to both 'standard' and advanced cryptics is Don Manley's *Crossword Manual* (Chambers).

Crossword Clubs
For the real enthusiast, there is the Crossword Club. Their monthly magazine *Crossword* contains tough puzzles and interesting features. Details from: The Editor, Coombe Farm, Coombe Lane, Awbridge, Romsey, Hants SO51 0HN.

Chambers
CRYPTIC CROSSWORDS
and How to Solve Them

Key to
Clue Types and Devices

a Double or multiple definitions
b Single definition
c Anagram:
　　i) Simple
　　ii) Complex
d Split
e Sandwich
f Takeaway sandwich
g Reverse direction
h Hidden word
i Sound effects
j Takeaway
k Moving letter
l Substituted letter
m Alternate letters
n Letter positions
　　i) Initials or last letters
　　ii) Specifically placed letters
o Abbreviations, numbers and
　　symbols
p Misleading punctuation
　　i) Misleading marks or
　　　　absence of them
　　ii) Words falsely run together
　　　　or separated
　　iii) False upper or lower
　　　　case letters
q Literary, historical or artistic
　　references
r Reference to another clue
s Archaic indicator
t Miscellaneous
u Definition part of device

DETAILED EXPLANATIONS APPEAR ON PAGES 9 - 16

Common abbreviations and clue equivalents

AB	seaman
AC	current, account
ACC	account, bill
AD	modern, advertisement
AG	silver
AI	(= A1) first class
B	black, born, bowled, note
BA	graduate, scholar
BR	railways, trains
C	100, about, conservative, roughly
CA	about, accountant, roughly
CC	200, volume
CE	church
CH	child, church, companion
CIA	spies
CO	care of, commanding officer, company
CR	credit
CU	copper
D	500, dead, died, many, note, penny
DA	(American) lawyer
DD	theologian
DI	Diana, princess
DR	doctor
E	East(ern), energy, note
EA	each
EC	City, London district
ED	journalist
EG	for example/instance, say
EP	disc, record
ER	Queen
EX	former, one-time
F	female, feminine, loud, note
FE	iron
FF	very loud
FR	father, French
FT	feet, foot
G	gramme, lightweight, note
GG	horse
GI	(American) soldier
H	hard, hospital, hydrogen
HE	ambassador, explosive
HP	never-never
HR	hour
I	one
IC	in charge
IE	that is, that's
II	eleven, side, team
IT	Italian, sex appeal

IV	four
IX	nine
K	constant, king, thousand
KO	decisive blow, knockout
L	50, lake, learner, left, Liberal, novice, pound
LAB	Labour
LB	pound
LP	record
LT	lieutenant
M	1 000, maiden, male, many, married, masculine
MA	graduate, scholar
MB	doctor
MD	1 500, doctor
MO	doctor, short time
MP	Member (of Parliament), politician
MS	writing
N	North(ern), pole
NB	note
NE	direction, north-east
NI	Ulster
NO	number, refusal
NT	books, part of bible
NW	direction, north-west
NY	New York
O	duck, love, nil, nothing, zero
OK	all right
OP	work
OS	outsize, sailor, very large
OT	books, part of bible
OZ	ounce, lightweight
P	page, parking, penny, piano, softly
PC	copper, policeman
PE	training
PER	by, for each
PM	afternoon, Prime Minister
PP	very softly
PR	price, public relations
PRO	expert, for, professional
PS	afterthought, second thoughts
Q	Queen
R	King, Queen, right, river
RA	artillery, artist, gunners
RD	road
RE	about, concerning
REP	agent, traveller

REV	priest, vicar
RM	jolly (Royal Marine)
RN	navy
RR	bishop
RT	right
RU	rugby
RY	lines, railway
S	pole, Saint, South(ern)
SA	South Africa/America, sex appeal
SE	direction, south-east
SP	betting, odds
SS	saints, ship, Sunday School
ST	good man, saint
T	car, model
TA	army, thanks, volunteers
TT	abstainer, dry, race, teetotal(ler)
U	(socially) acceptable, posh, universal, upper class
UK	Britain, United Kingdom
UN	United Nations, international organization
US	America(n), you and me
V	against, five, verse
VI	six
VOL	volume
W	West(ern)
X	cross, kiss, ten
XI	eleven, side, team
Y	yard, year
YR	year, your
ZZ	asleep, snoring

Roman numerals

I	one
II	two
IV	four
V	five
VI	six
IX	nine
X	ten
XI	eleven
XV	fifteen
L	fifty
C	hundred
CC	two hundred
D	five hundred
M	thousand
MD	fifteen hundred
MM	two thousand

Chambers
CRYPTIC CROSSWORDS
and How to Solve Them